P9-DET-493

Pistols and Revolvers

Originally published as *Revolvers et Pistolets* by Copyright S.A.

This edition published by Barnes & Noble, Inc.,
by arrangement with Coyright S.A.

1999 Barnes & Noble Books

ISBN 0-7607-1191-7

Printed and bound in Spain

99 00 01 02 MC 9 8 7 6 5 4 3 2 1

BPSL

Pistols and Revolvers

Jean-Noël Mouret

CONTENTS

All weapons illustrated in this book are shown actual size unless otherwise stated.

Left: Smith & Wesson revolver in its holster.

P226
MADE IN W.GERMANY
U 485 540
9 mm Para
U 485 540

HAND GUNS: THE MYTHS AND THE REALITY

We are at least as fascinated by hand guns as we are afraid of them. Westerns, detective novels, gangster movies, spy stories have made pistols and revolvers so commonplace that they have become part of our everyday speech. So long as they remain figures of speech they keep their appeal. In fact, nobody ever wants to find themselves in the role of a real hero faced with a real gun. The deadly thrill of the pistol duel embodies all our feelings of attraction and repulsion in a single instance.

Even so, hand guns have a charm and beauty all of their own. And shooting is a good way to learn concentration. The weapon becomes a perfect extension of hand and eye. Anyone who has ever handled the ergonomic grip of a competition weapon will know that instant feeling of balance and well-being.

Hand guns are also amazing examples of technology and miniaturization. To have imagined and produced such strong, simple and reliable mechanisms, to have mastered materials capable of withstanding the enormous forces created by exploding gunpowder, and to have put all this into such a small space while still keeping the weight down to a few ounces, is nothing less than genius. Yet in the 19th century, unaided by sophisticated calculators and computers, gunsmiths were already designing hand guns that to this day can still demonstrate their quality and accuracy in shooting competitions.

Sig P 226 pistol.
Model 19 Smith & Wesson revolver.
(shown smaller than actual size).

S. 1876
Mre d'Armes
St Etienne
PATENTED APR 20.1897
COLT'S PT F.A. MFG CO.
HARTFORD CT. U.S.A.
UNITED STATES PROPERTY

Hand guns: their history and technical development

Hand guns, that is to say pistols and revolvers, are the ultimate stages in the miniaturization of hand-held firearms. The latter include rifles and carbines, which themselves derive from miniaturization of the cannon.

The first hand-held firearms were shoulder cannon. These were muzzle-loaders and first appeared around 1450. They were like miniature artillery pieces, and their powder charge was fired by a smoldering match. To fire the weapon, a sharpshooter would light his match, blow on it to make it burn hotter, and then ignite the powder. By the time he had done all this, his intended target probably had plenty of time to get out of the line of fire!

These early weapons were very soon widened and extended at the back end so that they could be steadied against the torso or shoulder of the user. This development was the ancestor of the rifle-butt. The cannon family tree then divided two ways. One branch evolved toward heavy artillery. The other grew toward individual weapons. Long-barreled weapons and hand guns developed side by side and shared the same technical advances.

The matchlock pistol, which first appeared long before the revolver, is a short-range, single shot weapon. The need for a more responsive and reliable firing mechanism than the match was recognized. This led to the wheellock.

The wheellock was probably invented early in the 16th century. It used a toothed wheel and flint, very much like the thumb-wheel lighters we are familiar with today. The wheel was turned

Chamelot-Delvigne revolver of 1873.
Colt 1911 pistol.

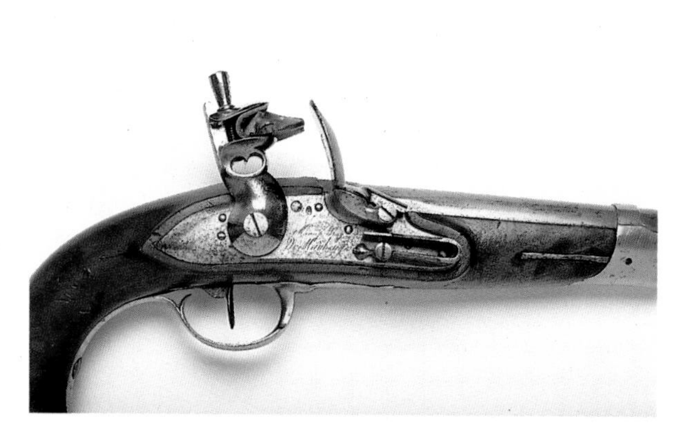

A flintlock ready to fire. The hammer is raised (or cocked) and the frizzen is lowered.

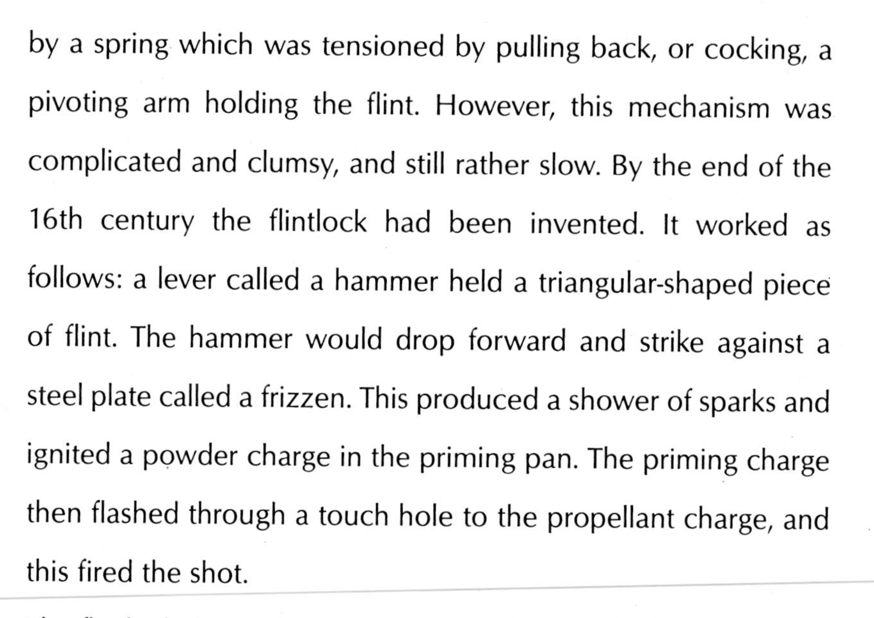

by a spring which was tensioned by pulling back, or cocking, a pivoting arm holding the flint. However, this mechanism was complicated and clumsy, and still rather slow. By the end of the 16th century the flintlock had been invented. It worked as follows: a lever called a hammer held a triangular-shaped piece of flint. The hammer would drop forward and strike against a steel plate called a frizzen. This produced a shower of sparks and ignited a powder charge in the priming pan. The priming charge then flashed through a touch hole to the propellant charge, and this fired the shot.

The flintlock developed in two stages: the so-called "rogue" lock, where the priming pan cover had to be opened by hand before firing, and the flintlock proper, with a one-piece frizzen and pan cover that did not need to be opened. The flintlock remained in use until 1850. Even so, it was still fairly slow and proved to be a particular problem in wet weather, when there was a good chance that the powder in the pan would get damp.

The next decisive step was the fulminate priming cap. This is a percussion cap, and still used to this day. It consists of a slim copper capsule containing a small amount of explosive material mixed with adhesive. The cap was placed over a small tube or duct (called a chamber) and struck with a firing-pin (also referred to as a hammer). This detonated the fulminate, causing it to flash through the chamber, ignite the gunpowder and so fire the shot. Being a very quick way of lighting the propellant charge, it improved accuracy and gave a higher initial velocity to the bullet. The new system was also more compact than the flintlock.

Today's highly sophisticated priming cap is set in the middle of the cartridge base, but the firing method is exactly the same in principle.

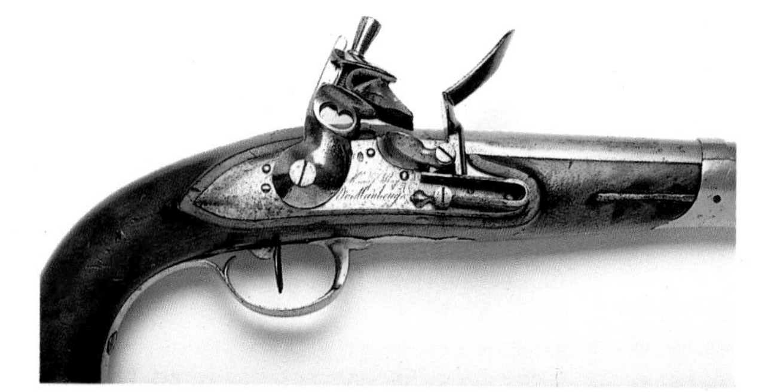

A flintlock after firing. The hammer is lowered, the frizzen is raised and the pan cover is open.

The percussion system at last made it possible to design and manufacture weapons that would fire more than one shot. There had in fact been some most ingenious attempts at producing flintlock repeating pistols or revolvers throughout the 18th century, but the results had been disappointing, since they were extremely complex and unreliable. The priming cap at last solved the problem.

Two hand guns then evolved up to about 1840-1850. One was the pepperbox, the other the revolver. The pepperbox had a revolving set of four to six barrels that lined up one at a time in front of the hammer. The revolver, on the other hand, had just one barrel and a revolving cylinder that held several bullets.

The pepperbox was clumsy and heavy. It was very soon overtaken by the revolver, which developed at runaway speed in the United States under the influence of some brilliant gunsmiths whose names we still know. These included Samuel Colt and Eliphalet Remington, as well as the famous partnership of Horace Smith and Daniel Baird Wesson, formed in 1852.

In fact it was Smith & Wesson who developed yet another decisive improvement, the metal cartridge, and put an end to the long and tedious business of reloading with gunpowder and ball. This new form of ammunition also made it possible to design pistols in which the gas produced as the weapon was fired could be used to drive the next cartridge into position for firing. So it was that the first automatic pistols appeared, around 1890.

Hand guns developed steadily from then on, still based on the principles laid down in the 19th century. In about 1960, two Americans, Robert Mainhardt and Art Bielh, designed the M.B.A. 13 mm Gyrojet. This looked like a pistol but was in fact a miniaturized rocket-launcher. Unfortunately it lacked power and accuracy, and so was a failure.

Percussion pistol ready to fire. The hammer is cocked and gives a clear view of the chamber that takes the priming cap (priming cap not present).

Percussion pistol after firing. The hammer is lowered. It fits completely over the tube and protects the shooter from the flash of the priming cap

SCH 26
Made in Germany
SCH 26
HK 46
HK 46

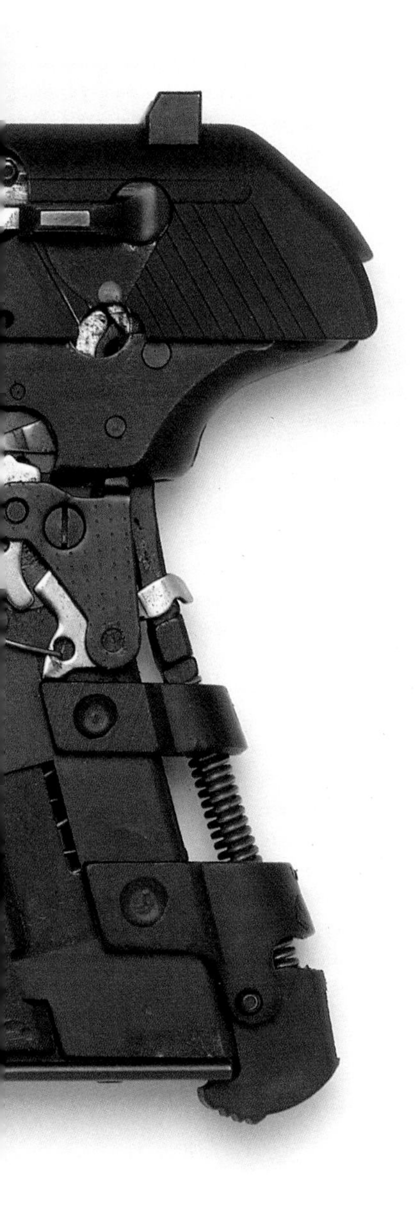

PISTOLS: HOW THEY WORK

As is generally known, a hand gun is fired by pulling a lever called a trigger. This is linked through other levers inside the weapon to the firing pin, or hammer, which detonates the cartridge. This also applies to revolvers, rifles, carbines and automatic machine pistols.

It should also be mentioned that although most pistols are said to be "automatic," in fact this is not always the case. An automatic weapon keeps firing all the time the trigger is pulled and the weapon is loaded. This is the situation with machine-guns and machine pistols set to fire in bursts. In fact, on most pistols the trigger has to be pulled for each shot, so they are really semi-automatic weapons. However, the expression "automatic" is now so common that it will be used throughout this book.

An automatic uses the force of the gas produced by the exploding gunpowder. The breech block recoils under the pressure. This movement ejects the spent cartridge case and drives the next cartridge from its magazine or loading clip into position for firing. In this way the weapon is readied for firing again at a very rapid rate.

This type of firing mechanism is of very sophisticated construction and has to be maintained with great care to prevent jamming. The caliber of the ammunition must also be carefully matched to the weapon.

Cut-away views of automatic pistols (shown smaller than actual size).
Upper picture: Heckler & Koch P9.
Lower picture: Heckler & Koch P7.

Revolvers: How They Work

A revolver is more rugged than an automatic pistol. It is not much affected by dust and does not jam, which explains its enormous success. On the other hand it has no recoil-absorbing mechanism. Depending on the type of cylinder, a reasonable size weapon can hold as many as nine shots.

It works very simply. The cylinder revolves on a spindle and contains several (usually five or six) chambers, each holding a cartridge.

Early models are said to be "single-action," that is, the hammer must be manually cocked for each shot before the trigger is pulled. Cocking the weapon rotates the cylinder and aligns the next loaded chamber with the barrel, and so on.

The "double action" mechanism, which eventually took over, cocks and fires the weapon each time the trigger is pulled. At first, the required trigger pressure was heavy enough to spoil the accuracy of the shot. There have since been many improvements which have tended to cure this fault.

Spent cartridge cases are ejected by swinging the cylinder out to the side and pressing on a star-shaped extractor. In the earliest models, the cylinder was removed by swinging the barrel downward. The guns are loaded in exactly the same way.

A stripped down Smith & Wesson .357 Magnum revolver.

AMMUNITION AND ACCESSORIES

Another point about the words we use. Pistols and revolvers are not loaded with bullets, but with metal-clad cartridges. The cartridge, which is a self-contained round of ammunition, consists of the bullet itself, the propellant charge (or gunpowder) and the primer cap, all housed in a copper jacket.

The bullet itself may be all-lead (round, snub-nosed or shaped like a truncated cone), or semi-jacketed (partly copper-clad) or jacketed (fully copper-clad). The choice depends on the required effect. The all-lead bullet produces a high force on impact. The jacketed bullet has high penetrating power. The semi-jacketed bullet is a compromise. Similarly, a conical bullet, a snub-nosed bullet and a hollow-nosed bullet behave very differently on impact. The conical bullet pierces, the hollow-nose causes explosive damage.

There are other kinds of ammunition of widely differing types, such as the shot-filled cartridge. Instead of containing a bullet this has a plastic cylinder filled with small lead shot. There are plastic cartridges with plastic bullets for shooting practise; and pellets for air pistols and gas guns.

All of this brings us naturally to the question of calibers, or more particularly, how to express them. In America they are usually given in thousandths of an inch (an inch is equal to 2.54 centimeters, abbreviated to 2.54 cm). In most of Europe, caliber is expressed in millimeters, with a millimeter being one-tenth of a centimeter.

Aimpoint 5000 telescopic sight.

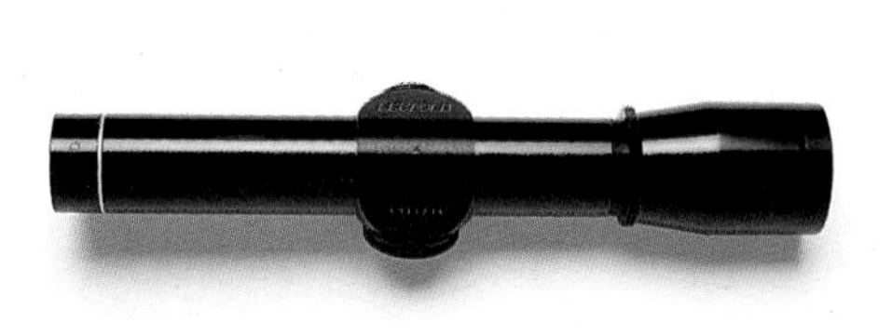

Leupold telescopic sight.

Laser aiming system, showing the laser transmitter and the connecting cable.

We can then draw up a conversion table as follows:

United States	Europe
.22	5.6 mm
.25	6.35 mm
.30	7.62 mm
.32	8.1 mm
.357	9 mm
.38	9.6 mm
.44	11.17 mm
.45	11.43 mm

These measurements describe the cartridge diameter, not the length, which may be given in millimeters. By this method, the expressions 9x19 or 9x21 are used to describe cartridges that are 9 mm in diameter and 19 or 21 mm long. As often as not the length is given as a name, such as .22 Long Rifle, .38 Special, .44 Magnum, 9 mm Parabellum, 9 mm Makarov, and so on.

There have, of course, been plenty of other calibers, none of them lasting for very long, such as the enormous .577 (14.65 mm) and .6 (15.34 mm). The picture gets even more confused by the tolerances that certain revolvers allow, being officially cataloged as .45/.455 (that is, 11.43 mm to 11.55 mm).

Of the many accessories available to the shooter, the best known are the telescopic sight and the silencer. In some countries, telescopic sights on hand guns are only used for target shooting. In the United States, where hunting with pistols and revolvers is permitted, most hand guns used for hunting are fitted with one.

The telescopic sight, or sighting telescope, should not be

confused with shooting spectacles. In fact, not all optical sights magnify the field of view. Those of the non-magnifying type are actually very light sensitive, and pick out the target so that the shooter can concentrate on it. On magnifying sights the degree of magnification can be altered.

The movies have given the silencer (or sound moderator) legendary status. In fact, it muffles the explosion but does not silence it completely. It is a fat tube that fits on the end of a gun barrel, and consists of an internal barrel riddled with dozens of holes that let the exhaust gases escape outward to an external jacket. The gases swirl through a labyrinth of baffle-plates between the internal barrel and the jacket, losing strength in the process. The bullet emerges at below the speed of sound, noiselessly followed by a gentle stream of gas.

A laser sighting system has recently become available. It consists of a small, ruby-red laser transmitter that can be switched on from the grip. The beam touches the target and tells the shooter whether the gun is properly aimed.

There are many other accessories for the hand gun user. They include ear-defenders, which are essential equipment on firing ranges; protective spectacles, some fitted with opaque or iris-diaphragm shutters to aid sighting and aiming; counterweights that can change a gun's center of gravity and balance the weapon to fit the sporting shooter; ergonomically designed left-handed grips; and so on.

Many other accessories could also be mentioned, such as interchangeable sights. Some light-sensitive models can be used as night sights. There are also gun maintenance products, all of them vital, but too numerous to mention, and more properly belonging to the field of precision engineering.

Protective goggles for the shooter, with frosted shutter and iris-diaphragm attachment.

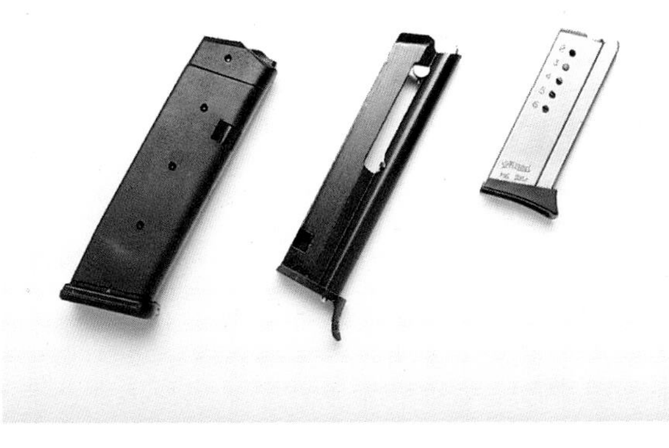

Different kinds of ammunition clips for automatic pistols.

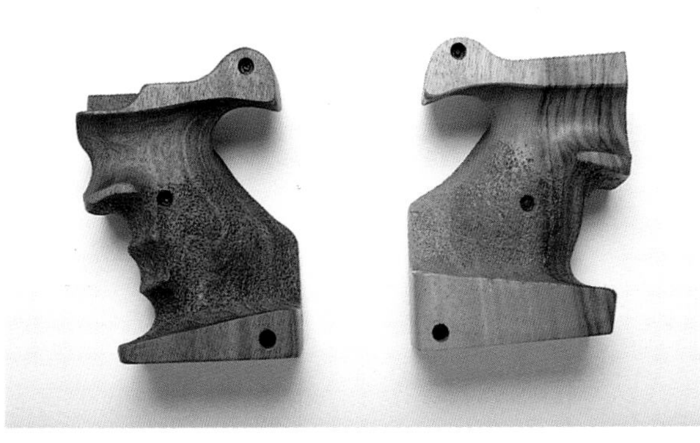

Ergonomically designed sporting pistol grips. The left-handed model is on the left and the right-handed model on the right.

SMITH & WESSON
TRADE
MARK
REG. U.S. PAT. OFF.

Revolvers

The modern revolver has not evolved much since the end of the 19th century. There have been many new models but no major developments. Some improvements centered on taking advantage of sophisticated new heat treatment processes to use lighter, stronger metals. Some made weapons safer, not least of all in case a loaded weapon is accidentally dropped, while others involved the use of more powerful cartridges. By way of example, Smith & Wesson developed the .357 Magnum in 1935 and the .44 Magnum in 1956.

Both loading and firing systems – single and double action – still coexist, and each has its following, though double action is far more widely used.

The market is dominated mainly by American manufacturers such as Smith & Wesson, Ruger, and Colt. Other firms include Taurus of Brazil and Astra of Spain.

Revolvers are made in three sizes. "Small" revolvers are light and sturdy, from 6 to 9.5 inches in length (15 cm to 24 cm), with barrels between two and four inches long (some 5 cm to 10 cm). "Medium" revolvers are from about 6.5 to 11 inches long with barrels from two to eight inches long (some 17 cm to 28 cm). "Large" revolvers have an overall length of 9.5 to about 14 inches (24 cm to 35 cm) and barrels between four and eight inches long (from about 10 cm to 21 cm). The variations in size are due to the different barrel lengths that are available for the same model, ranging from two inches (5 cm) to eight inches (21 cm).

The only noticeable differences in appearance relate to the cartridge extractor located under the barrel, which may be either visible or protected by a housing that runs the whole length of the barrel.

Smith & Wesson "Centennial" Revolver (shown larger than actual size).

Model 60 revolver by Smith & Wesson.
4th category weapon.
5-shot revolver.
2-inch (5 cm) barrel (available as 3-inch – 7.5 cm).
Caliber .38 Special Smith & Wesson.
All stainless steel construction, wooden grip plates.
Weight: 1 lb 6 oz (0.624 kg) unloaded.
Made by Smith & Wesson (USA).

The Model 60 Smith & Wesson is a close-quarters defensive weapon combining compactness with fire-power.

Model 649 revolver by Smith & Wesson.
4th category weapon.
5-shot revolver.
2-inch (5 cm) barrel.
Caliber .38 Special Smith & Wesson.
All stainless steel construction, wooden grip plates.
Weight: 1 lb 4 oz (0.567 kg) unloaded.
Made by Smith & Wesson (USA).

The ultra-slim Model 649 Smith & Wesson, called the "Centennial," is noted for its inset firing-pin. This means the weapon can easily be drawn without becoming entangled in clothing.

Model 63 revolver by Smith & Wesson.
4th category weapon.
6-shot revolver.
2-inch (5 cm) barrel (available as 4-inch – 10 cm).
Caliber .22 Long Rifle.
All stainless steel construction, wooden grip plates.
Weight: 1 lb 6 oz (0.624 kg) unloaded.
Made by Smith & Wesson (USA).

The Model 63 Smith & Wesson has an adjustable rearsight specially for shooting practice.

Astra revolver.
4th category weapon.
6-shot revolver.
Caliber .357 Magnum.
4-inch (10 cm) barrel.
All stainless steel construction, wooden grip plates.
Weight: About 2 lb 3 oz (1 kg) unloaded.
Made by Astra (Spain).

The most powerful gun is not always the one you would expect.... The impressive-looking Smith & Wesson, with its ergonomic grip and adjustable rearsight, is a small caliber .22 Long Rifle sporting weapon. Despite its meek appearance the Astra, with its .357 Magnum caliber, is altogether a more formidable weapon.

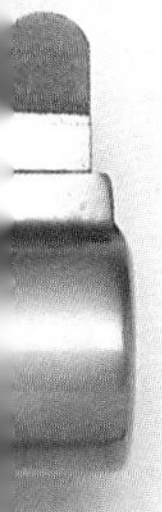

APPEARANCES CAN BE DECEPTIVE...

Model 617 revolver by Smith & Wesson.
4th category weapon.
6-shot revolver.
Caliber .22 Long Rifle.
4-inch (10 cm) barrel (available as 2-inch and 6-inch – 5 cm and 15 cm).
All stainless steel construction, wooden grip plates.
Weight: 3 lb 6 oz (1.530 kg) unloaded.
Made by Smith & Wesson (USA).

These two weapons are absolutely identical apart from the length of their barrels. The differences affect not only their weight, but more particularly their centre of gravity. The longer the barrel, the more accurate the shot. On the other hand, when choosing a weapon it is important to distinguish between muscle power and the amount of weight you can carry.

Model 586 revolver by Smith & Wesson.
4th category weapon.
6-shot revolver.
Caliber .357 Magnum (.38 Special Smith & Wesson)
4-inch (10 cm) barrel
(available as 4-inch and 6-inch – 10 cm and 15 cm).
All steel construction, wooden grip plates.
Weight: 2 lb 10 oz (1.2 kg) unloaded.
Made by Smith & Wesson (USA).

Model 586 revolver by Smith & Wesson.
4th category weapon.
6-shot revolver. Caliber .357 Magnum (.38 Special Smith & Wesson).
6-inch (15 cm) barrel
(available as 4-inch and 6-inch – 10 cm and 15 cm).
All steel construction, wooden grip plates.
Weight: 2 lb 15 oz (1.350 kg) unloaded.
Made by Smith & Wesson (USA).

FOR A FEW INCHES

Model 686 revolver by Smith & Wesson.
4th category weapon.
6-shot revolver.
Caliber .357 Magnum (.38 Special Smith & Wesson).
4-inch (10 cm) barrel (available as 2 1/2-inch, 4-inch, 6-inch and 8 3/8-inch – 6.25 cm, 10 cm, 15 cm and 21.25 cm).
All stainless steel construction, wooden grip plates.
Weight: 2 lb 9 oz (1.16 kg) unloaded.
Made by Smith & Wesson (USA).

Model 686 revolver by Smith & Wesson.
4th category weapon.
6-shot revolver.
Caliber .357 Magnum (.38 Special Smith & Wesson).
6-inch (15 cm) barrel (available as 2 1/2-inch, 4-inch, 6-inch and 8 3/8-inch – 6.25 cm, 10 cm, 15 cm and 21.25 cm).
All steel construction, wooden grip plates.
Weight: 2 lb 13 oz (1.3 kg) unloaded.
Made by Smith & Wesson (USA).

These two medium-size, double action revolvers have a very easy firing action and balanced design. They are standard issue to police forces in the United States.

THE SHERIFF'S FRIENDS

Astra revolver.
4th category weapon.
6-shot revolver.
Caliber .44 Magnum.
8-inch (20 cm) barrel.
All steel construction, wooden grip plates.
Weight: About 3 lb 4 1/2 oz (1.5 kg) unloaded.
Made by Astra (Spain).

Two "weighty" weapons that call to mind a number of American TV series ....

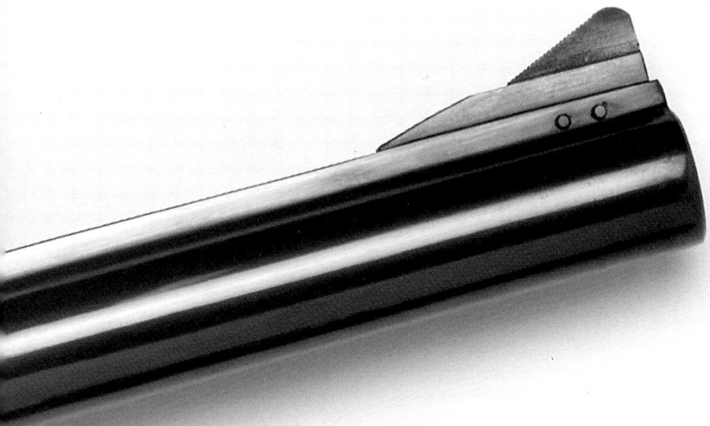

Model 29 revolver by Smith & Wesson.
4th category weapon.
6-shot revolver.
Caliber .44 Magnum (.44 Special Smith & Wesson).
4-inch (10 cm) barrel (available as 4-inch, 6-inch and 8 3/8-inch – 10 cm, 15 cm and 21.25 cm).
All steel construction, wooden grip plates.
Weight: About 2 lb 10 oz (1.2 kg) unloaded.
Made by Smith & Wesson (USA).

LARGE CALIBER WEAPONS

Model GP 100 revolver by Ruger.
4th category weapon.
6-shot revolver.
Caliber .357. 6-inch (15 cm) barrel (available as 3-inch, 4-inch and 6-inch – 7.5 cm, 10 cm and 15 cm).
All steel construction, wood and rubber grip plates.
Weight: About 2 lb 10 oz (1.2 kg) unloaded.
Made by Sturm, Ruger & Co (USA).

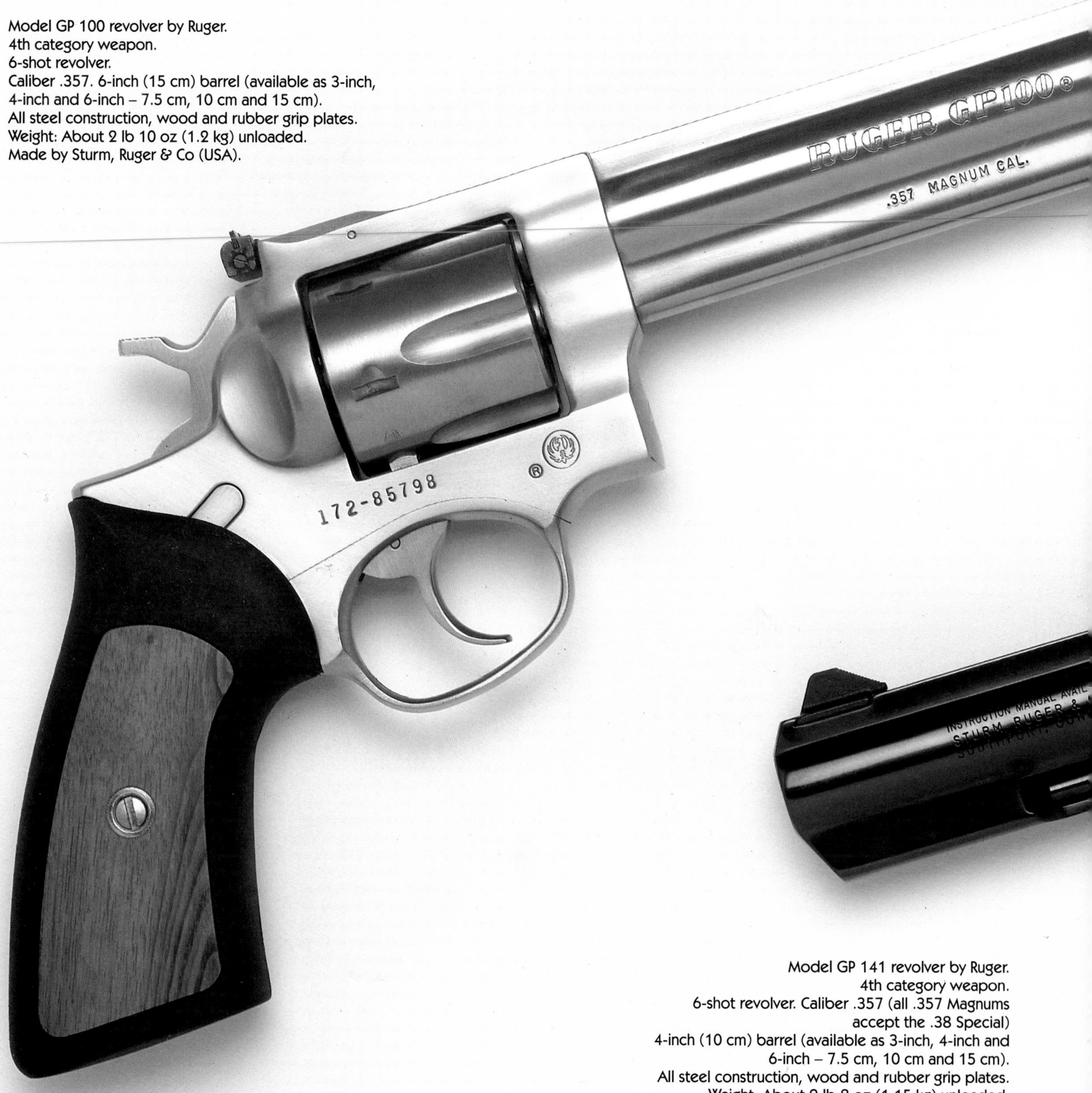

Model GP 141 revolver by Ruger.
4th category weapon.
6-shot revolver. Caliber .357 (all .357 Magnums accept the .38 Special)
4-inch (10 cm) barrel (available as 3-inch, 4-inch and 6-inch – 7.5 cm, 10 cm and 15 cm).
All steel construction, wood and rubber grip plates.
Weight: About 2 lb 8 oz (1.15 kg) unloaded.
Made by Sturm, Ruger & Co (USA).

Both these double action revolvers belong to the GP 100 series. This range represents the pinnacle of technical advancement in revolvers. All the main parts are micro-cast in chromium-molybdenum steel. The firing mechanism is stainless steel. Ruger champions and "promotes" the use of micro-casting techniques in the production of hand guns and rifles. Weapons made in this way are extremely tough and hardwearing.

SOPHISTICATED AND GOOD LOOKING

Mre Impale de
Châtellerault
MANUFRANCE-SAINT-ETIENNE

Pistols

The pistol was largely overshadowed by the revolver in the 19th century, but made a strong comeback around 1900 with the invention of the automatic. Some famous names were first heard around that time, including Mauser, Luger and Borchardt.

The automatic pistol operates in much the same way as the early machine-guns. The recoil energy generated by firing a round is used to eject the spent cartridge case and drive the next cartridge into position for the next shot. As the breech recoils, it activates the ejection and reloading mechanisms. Automatics are in reality semi-automatic, since the trigger has to be pulled for every shot (except for automatic machine pistols). It has to be done this way in order to keep the weapon aimed and avoid emptying the magazine in a single burst. Since the gun is reloaded every time it is fired, a hand-operated safety catch locks the mechanism whenever necessary.

All pistols currently in production work this way. The main variants concern caliber, which affects the recoil energy produced by the ammunition. The pistol-grip houses a magazine of cartridges which can be quickly replaced when empty.

The main advantages of the pistol over the revolver are its thinness and its high loading capacity. The revolver is limited by the size of the cylinder. On the other hand, because the pistol is more complex and therefore more likely to jam, it has to be maintained with great care. The ammunition must also be perfectly made and the caliber must be a perfect match for the weapon.

19th century percussion pistol.
Manufrance pistol "Le Français," caliber 6.35 drop barrel.

Model 2201 pistol by Smith & Wesson.
4th category weapon.
10-shot magazine.
Caliber .22 Long Rifle.
Available with 4 1/2-inch or 6-inch (11.4 cm or 15 cm) barrel length.
All stainless steel construction.
Weight: 1 lb 1 1/2 oz (500 g) unloaded.
Made by Smith & Wesson (USA).

Small, single action automatic, ideal for self defense and target practise.

Model TPH pistol by Walther.
4th category weapon.
Caliber .22 Long Rifle (available as 6.35 mm).
6-shot magazine.
All steel construction.
Weight: 11 oz (315 g) unloaded.
Made by Interarms (USA).

Compact version of the famous Walther PP and PPK automatic pistols. Mainly a pocket-size self-defense weapon.

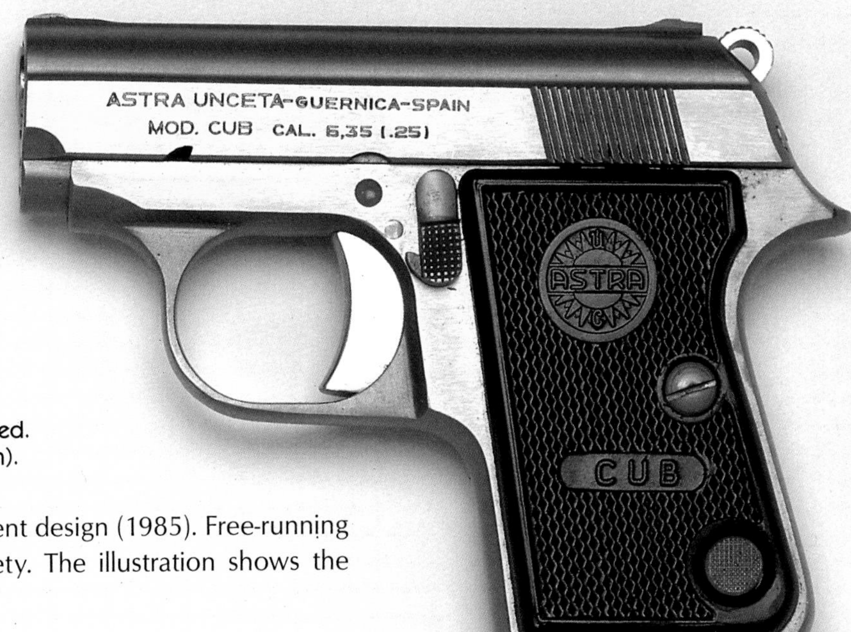

Model Cub pistol by Astra.
4th category weapon.
Caliber 6.35 mm.
7-shot magazine.
All steel construction.
Weight: 12½ oz (360 g) unloaded.
Made by Astra Llama S.A. (Spain).

Compact automatic of recent design (1985). Free-running breech and magazine safety. The illustration shows the stainless steel version.

Model P 226 pistol by Sig.
1st category weapon.
Caliber 9 mm Parabellum.
15-shot staggered magazine.
Steel and light alloy construction.
Weight: 1 lb 10 oz (740 g) unloaded.
Made by Sauer (Germany).

This equivalent of the Beretta 92, the Sig P 226 is developed from the Sig P 220, which it closely resembles. Intended for military use. Other variants of this model are available: the P 228, the P 229, the P 220 and the P 225.

Model 92 FS pistol by Beretta.
1st category weapon.
Caliber 9 mm Parabellum.
15-shot staggered magazine.
Chassis constructed of light alloy (Ergal).
Weight: 2 lb 1 oz unloaded.
Made by Pietro Beretta (Italy).

HAND GUNS FOR THE ARMED FORCES AND THE POLICE

The Beretta 92 is a high-quality military hand gun. Designed in 1976, there are now many derivatives, including the 92 FC, 92 FK, 92 S, 92 S-1, 92 SB, 92 SB-F (known as the 92 F), 93 R, 96 and 96 I. These variants were produced at the request of many police forces around the world which use this gun. It has been manufactured under license in France by MAS since 1988, where it is known as the Giat MAS G 1.

Model 82 BB pistol by Beretta.
4th category weapon.
Caliber 7.65 mm.
9+1-shot magazine.
Steel construction, aluminum body, wooden grip plates.
Weight: 1 lb 7 oz (660 g) unloaded.
Made by Pietro Beretta (Italy).

Development of the Beretta 81. Similar to the Model 84, the only real difference being the caliber, 7.65 mm instead of 9 mm Short.

Desert Eagle pistol.
4th category weapon.
Caliber .357 Magnum (available as .44 Magnum).
9-shot magazine (7-shot as .44 Magnum).
All steel or steel and alloy construction.
Weight: All steel: 3 lb 14 oz (1.760 kg); alloy: 3 lb 4 oz (unloaded weight in each case).
Made by IMI (Israel Military Industries) (Israel).

The Desert Eagle is a large caliber automatic pistol. It was first produced in 1985 as a development of the 1983 Eagle. It is designed for accuracy at medium range (650 feet – 200 meters), while most pistols are designed to be effective at 200 feet (60 meters).

Model 1911 pistol by Springfield.
1st category weapon.
Caliber .40 Smith & Wesson.
8-shot magazine.
All steel construction, wooden grip plates.
Weight: 2 lb 7 oz (1.1 kg) unloaded.
Made by Springfield Armory (USA).

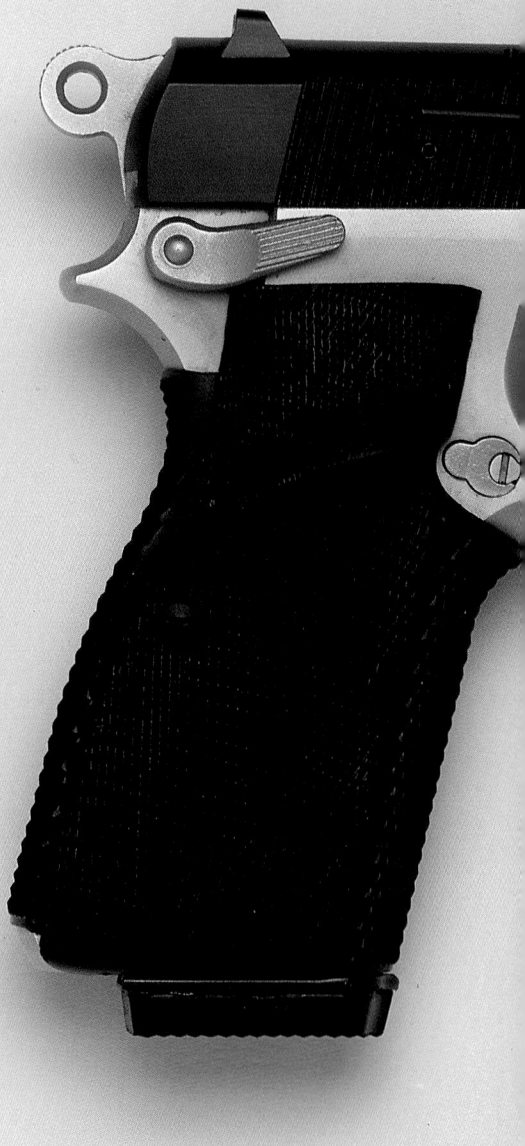

This hand gun was standard issue for the US Army for decades. A development of this model gave rise to the Springfield Trophy Master, known as the "Distinguished Pistol," intended as a sporting weapon (see page 88).

Model GP Competition pistol by Browning.
1st category weapon.
Caliber 9 mm Parabellum (also available as 9 mm Luger).
13 to 20-shot magazine (depending on magazine type).
All steel construction.
Weight: 2 lb 3 oz (1 kg) unloaded.
Made by Fabrique Nationale d'Armes de Guerre (Belgium).

AT HOME ON BATTLEFIELD OR SHOOTING RANGE

Originally a military hand gun, this pistol has been redesigned as a sporting weapon, with a counterweight, an adjustable trigger and rearsight, a thumb rest and a wrap-around rubber grip.

Model 19 pistol by Glock.
1st category weapon.
Caliber 9 mm Parabellum.
17-shot magazine.
Made of composite materials.
Weight: 1 lb 7 oz (660 g) unloaded.
Made by Glock GmbH (Austria).

This recent design (1988) is a very light and compact version of the Glock 17. Apart from the steel slide, it is made entirely of composite materials (polypropylene).

TECHNICAL BREAKTHROUGH

Model P7 M13 pistol from HK.
1st category weapon.
Caliber 9 mm Parabellum.
13-shot staggered magazine.
All steel construction.
Weight: 2 lb 7 oz (1.1 kg) unloaded.
Made by Heckler & Koch (Germany).

Regulation hand gun for the German Police, the HK P7 M13 is noted for two original features. First, the automatic action is not powered directly from the exhaust gases but by a gas recovery system, giving it a very gentle action. Also, the hammer is cocked by squeezing a lever built into the pistol grip.

Model 5906 pistol by Smith & Wesson.
1st category weapon.
Caliber 9 mm Parabellum.
14-shot magazine.
All steel construction.
Weight: 3 lb 14 oz (1.75 kg) unloaded.
Made by Smith & Wesson (USA).

The classic automatic, fairly heavy, but reliable.

This weapon is similar to the Smith & Wesson, but was designed more recently (1985). It is much lighter and has a larger magazine. The external catch is ambidextrous.

Model A-90 pistol by Astra.
1st category weapon.
Caliber 9 mm Parabellum.
15-shot magazine.
All steel construction.
Weight: 2 lb 3 oz (985 g) unloaded.
Made by Astra Llama S.A. (Spain).

Model AT 2000 S pistol by Sphinx.
1st category weapon.
Caliber 9 mm Parabellum.
15-shot magazine.
All steel construction.
Weight: 2 lb 3 oz (1 kg) unloaded.
Made by Sphinx (Switzerland).

Like the Italian Tanfoglio and the Israeli Jericho, the Sphinx is one of the many pistols derived directly from the Czech CZ, with the same general layout and format but a rather more sophisticated appearance.

THE CZECH CONNECTION

Model 85 pistol by CZ.
1st category weapon.
Caliber 9 mm Parabellum.
15-shot magazine.
All steel construction.
Weight: 2 lb 3 oz (1 kg) unloaded.
Made by Ceska-Zbrojovka (Czech Republic).

This is the ambidextrous version of the CZ 75 pistol, designed in 1986. It is a double action, Browning system weapon. The CZ series has had an influence on the design of many pistols around the world.

Model DES 69 U pistol by Unique.
4th category weapon.
Caliber .22 Long Rifle.
5 shots.
All steel construction, wooden grip.
Weight: 2 lb 3 oz (1 kg) unloaded.
Made by Unique (France).

ACCURACY WITH A PEACEFUL PURPOSE

This highly accurate, "hi-tech" sporting pistol, made entirely of carbon fiber (apart from the barrel and the breech), is used by the Swiss national shooting team.

Model 280 pistol by Hämmerli.
4th category weapon.
Caliber .22 Long Rifle.
10 shots.
Carbon fiber construction.
Weight: 2 lb 3 oz (1 kg) unloaded.
Made by Hämmerli (Switzerland).

AUTOMATIC MACHINE-PISTOLS

Machine pistols are among the larger members of the hand gun family. They get their name from the fact that they can operate either in semi-automatic mode (the trigger has to be pressed for each shot) or in fully automatic mode (the weapon keeps firing while the trigger is pressed). The mode is selected by means of a switch. This is usually on the left side of the gun. The selector switch often has a third position for safety.

Spent cartridges are ejected on the right, as with a conventional automatic pistol. The most common calibers are the 9 mm Parabellum and the 7.65.

They have high-capacity magazines that routinely extend beyond the pistol-grip. To make the weapon easier to hold, especially in automatic mode, most machine pistols have another grip for the left hand, usually below the barrel. This grip may be fixed, folding or detachable, depending on the design. Usually the weapon also has a folding or extending shoulder rest.

Because machine pistols are designed to operate in difficult conditions, they tend to be efficient rather than good looking, with generously proportioned firing mechanisms, pressed and painted sheet-steel construction, plastic grips, and a dull, matt, non-reflecting finish.

Micro UZI automatic machine-pistol viewed from the ejector side (open) (shown smaller than actual size).

ARS

The Micro UZI has been manufactured since 1985. It has a selector for firing in bursts, and a folding shoulder rest which can also be used as a hand grip. This is the military version of the UZI semi-automatic pistol, which was first developed in 1983-84. Design and development of the UZI range was begun in 1950 by an Israeli officer, Uzi Gal, and the first UZI machine pistols were made in 1953. The Micro UZI is intended mainly for military escort duties. It can be fired two-handed, from a vehicle if need be, and can also be hidden easily under clothing. As with all UZI weapons, it is influenced by the VZ 23 and VZ 25 machine pistols from the Czech Republic, and can match them with its quite exceptional simplicity and reliability.

THE MICRO UZI

Micro UZI machine pistol.
1st category weapon.
Caliber 9 mm Parabellum.
20, 25 or 32-shot staggered magazine.
All steel construction.
Weight: 4 lb 6 oz (2 kg) unloaded.
Made by Israel Military Industries (IMI) (Işrael).

Model M 61 Skorpion machine pistol.
1st category weapon.
Caliber 7.65 mm Browning.
10 or 20-shot magazine with overlapping cartridges.
All steel construction.
Weight: 3 lb 5 oz (1.5 kg) unloaded.
Made by Ceska-Zbrojovka (Czech Republic).

With its free-running breech and damped opening action, this machine pistol is more suited to defense than offense. It has one or two special features: curved magazine clips, a shoulder rest made of heavy gauge double steel rod that folds back over the weapon, and the ability to take a silencer.

THE SKORPION

The MAC 10 machine pistol.
1st category weapon.
Caliber .45 ACP or 9 mm Parabellum.
14 or 30-shot magazine with overlapping cartridges.
All steel construction.
Weight: 6 lb 3 oz (2.8 kg) unloaded.
Made by Ingram (USA).

The MAC 10, formerly the Ingram M 10, is directly influenced by the UZI machine pistol. Its light breech and damped opening action ensure a particularly high rate of fire (1200 rounds/minute). It can take a silencer. On the other hand, because of its size, and more especially its weight, it is more suited to special missions and "home" defense duties (such as defending buildings from external aggression).

THE MAC 10

Model M-4 Spectre machine pistol.
1st category weapon.
Caliber 9 mm Parabellum.
32-shot magazine.
All steel construction.
Weight: 6 lb 10 oz (3 kg) unloaded.
Made by SITES (Italy).

THE SPECTRE

Conventional machine pistol, designed for two-handed firing, with damped-opening breech action.

41745
S

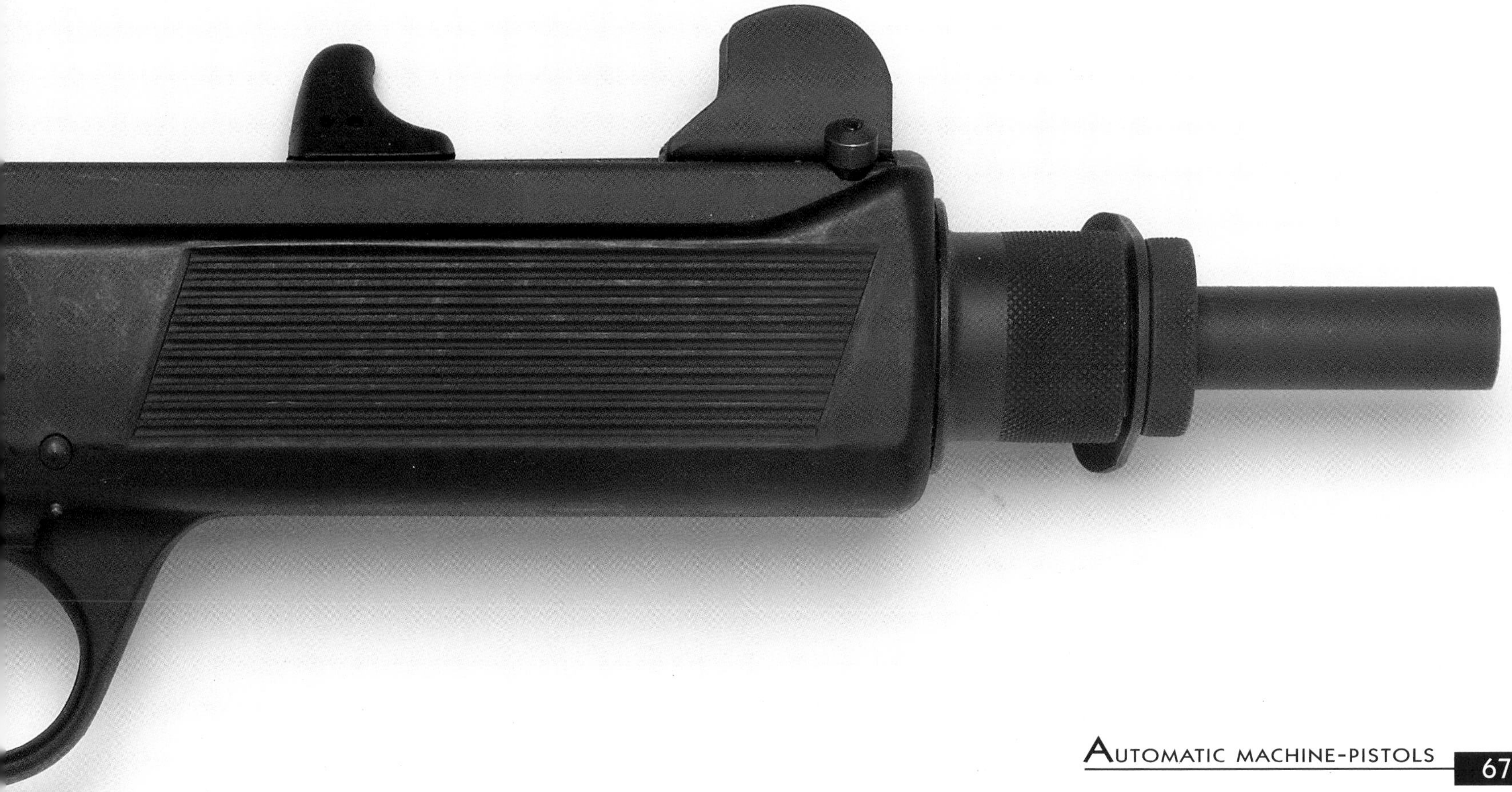

THE STEYR MP I 81

Model MP i 81 machine pistol by Steyr.
1st category weapon.
Caliber 9 x 19 mm Parabellum.
25 or 32-shot magazine with overlapping cartridges.
All steel construction.
Weight: 6 lb 6 oz (2.9 kg) unloaded.
Made by Steyr Mannlicher (Austria).

Highly compact tactical machine pistol, designed for special operations by specialist units.

THE STEYR MP i 69

Model MP i 69 machine pistol by Steyr.
1st category weapon.
Caliber 9 x 19 mm Parabellum.
25 or 32-shot magazine with overlapping cartridges.
All steel construction.
Weight: 6 lb 6 oz (2.9 kg) unloaded.
Made by Steyr Mannlicher (Austria).

The Steyr MP i 69 looks exactly the same as the MP i 81 on the previous pages, but uses a radically different cocking system. Whereas the MP i 81 has a conventional cocking lever, the MP i 69 is cocked by means of its shoulder sling. With the gun slung from the shoulder, a sharp forward tug is all it takes to cock the firing pin. This means it is always possible to keep one hand free.

40201
F
40201

HÄMMERLI

SHOOTING AS A SPORT

Shooting as a member of a club provides one of those rare opportunities for using a hand gun. Target practice is, above all, a school for self-discipline, self-control, concentration and inner calm.

There is a category for everyone: 10-meter target (30 feet); high-speed shooting at five rotating 25-meter targets (75 feet); 50-meter target (150 feet); shooting ranges; and so on.

There are several differences between sporting weapons and normal firearms. Among other things, the improved trigger action needs only very light finger pressure. Sights are interchangeable. Ergonomically designed grips can be customized to fit the shooter's hand, and are available in left-handed or right-handed versions.

This is also the field where problems receive some of the most original thinking, such as using compressed air or bottled CO2 to "fire" the round. Some of the most striking designs are also to be found among sporting weapons, such as the Hämmerli pistol shown here, which is a true "designer piece" hardly resembling a conventional pistol at all.

You need a license to take part in target shooting and also to own a firearm and the ammunition for it. Your nearest gunsmith will be able to tell you about your own local regulations.

Hämmerli sporting pistol and ear-defenders
(shown smaller than actual size).

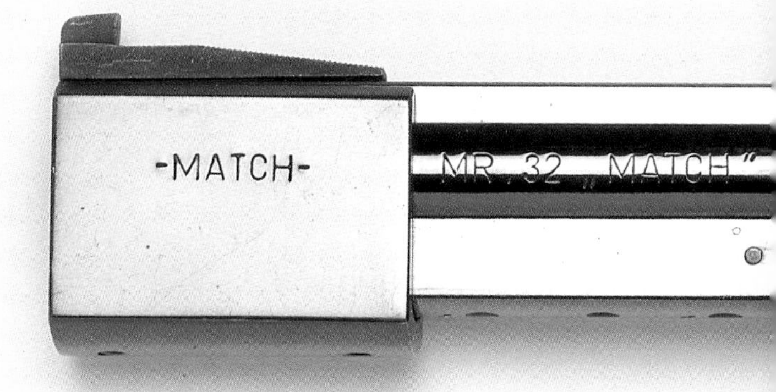

Model Sport revolver by Korth.
4th category weapon.
Caliber .22 Long Rifle.
6-shot.
All steel construction.
Weight: 2 lb 15 oz (1.35 kg) unloaded.
Made by Korth (Germany).

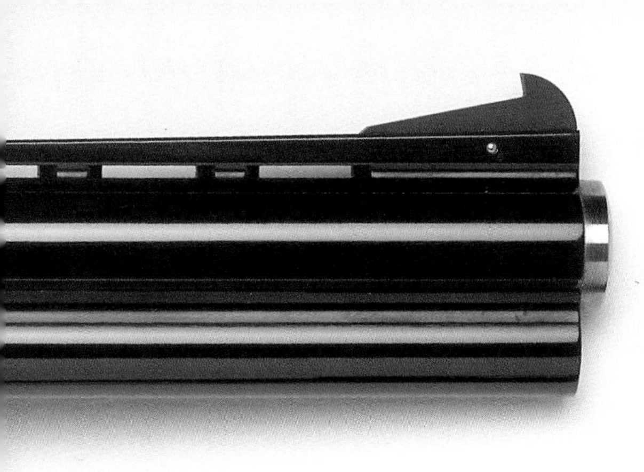

Model MR 32 revolver by Manurhin.
4th category weapon.
Caliber .32 SW Long Wadcutter.
6-shot.
All steel construction.
Weight: 2 lb 13 oz (1.270 kg) unloaded.
Made by Manurhin (France).

THE .22 LONG RIFLE

Buck Mark pistol by Browning.
4th category weapon.
Caliber .22 Long Rifle
10-shot.
All steel construction.
Weight: 2 lb 14 oz (1.3 kg) unloaded.
Made by Fabrique Nationale d'Armes de Guerre (Belgium).

Pistol for shooting competitions using metal silhouette targets.
Very much a sporting model.

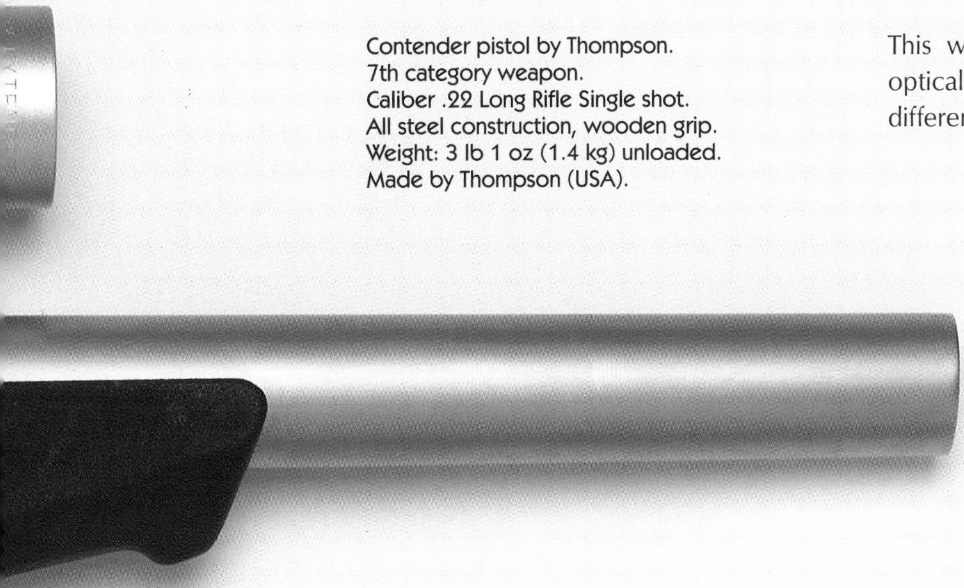

Contender pistol by Thompson.
7th category weapon.
Caliber .22 Long Rifle Single shot.
All steel construction, wooden grip.
Weight: 3 lb 1 oz (1.4 kg) unloaded.
Made by Thompson (USA).

This weapon is fitted with a Leupold 2x magnification optical sight. Although the weapons shown here look quite different, they are both very suitable for silhouette targets.

THE .22 LONG RIFLE

BROWNING ARMS COMPANY
MORGAN, UTAH U.S.A. &
MONTREAL, P.Q. CANADA

655NX01418

Master 52 pistol by Smith & Wesson.
4th category weapon.
Caliber .38 Special Smith & Wesson.
5-shot.
All steel construction, walnut grip plates.
Weight: 2 lb 7 oz (1.1 kg) unloaded.
Made by Smith & Wesson (USA).

This pistol was designed as a target weapon from the very start, as can be seen for instance from the beavertail at the rear of the handgrip, and the adjustable microclick rearsight.

THE .38 CALIBER

Model 14 revolver by Smith & Wesson.
4th category weapon.
Caliber .38 Special Smith & Wesson.
6-shot.
All steel construction, wooden grip.
Weight: 2 lb 7 oz (1.1 kg) unloaded.
Made by Smith & Wesson (USA).

Sporting weapon. Ergonomic grip, narrow hammer spur, light trigger.

This pistol for the 50-meter target (150 feet) won medals in the Olympic Games during the 1950s. It was the first weapon to be fitted with advanced features such as an ergonomic grip, a five-position adjustable trigger and finger pressure which could be independently varied from five up to one hundred grams ($^1/_{100}$ th oz to $3^1/_2$ oz).

Model 106 pistol by Hämmerli.
7th category weapon.
Caliber .22 Long Rifle.
Single shot.
All steel construction, wooden grip.
Weight: 2 lb 3 oz (1 kg) unloaded.
Made by Hämmerli (Switzerland).

OLYMPIC VETERANS

Model 602 pistol by FAS.
4th category weapon.
Caliber .22 Long Rifle.
Single shot.
All steel construction, wooden grip plates.
Weight: 2 lb 7 oz (1.1 kg).
Made by FAS (Italy).

Model 604 pistol by FAS.
Caliber 4.5 (aka .177)
Single shot.
All steel construction, wooden grip plates.
Weight: 2 lb 7 oz (1.1 kg).
Made by FAS (Italy).

Single shot pistol using compressed air and lead pellets.

SINGLE-SHOT WEAPONS

This simple, sturdy pistol is the ancestor of the compressed-air competition weapons. Almost all national records set in Europe and worldwide for the last twenty years were notched up with this weapon. It is still in production.

Model 65 pistol by Feinwerkbau.
Caliber 4.5.
Single shot.
All steel construction, wooden grip plates.
Weight: 2 lb 13 oz (1.280 kg).
Made by Westinger & Altenburger (Germany).

This CO_2-powered revolver is an inexpensive copy of the Colt Python .357 and ideal for the hobby shooter.

Crosman revolver.
Caliber 4.5.
6-shot.
Available with 4-inch and 6-inch barrel (10 and 15 cm).
Weight: 1 lb 15½ oz (0.9 kg).
Made by Crosman (USA).

COMPRESSED AIR VERSUS CO_2

Model 102 two-stage compressed-air pistol by Feinwerkbau.
7th category weapon.
Pistol firing single lead pellets.
Caliber 4.5.
All steel mechanism, ergonomic wooden grip.
Weight: 2 lb 9´ oz (1.18 kg) (counterweight extra).
Made by Westinger & Altenburger (Germany).

AIR-PISTOLS WITH TWO-STAGE COMPRESSION

This pistol has a two-lever cocking mechanism that considerably reduces the effort needed to compress the air (just 11 to 13 lbs of effort, or 5 to 6 kilograms, instead of the usual 20 lbs/9 kilograms). The air is compressed in two stages. Both levers are opened as far as they will go, drawing air into the compression chamber. Closing the smaller lever then produces first-stage compression. Full compression is then obtained by closing the larger lever. With this very practical cocking system the shooter can save energy and concentrate on making the shot.
To improve accuracy, the muzzle is designed to ensure the lead pellet is not deflected by a vortex on emerging.
Like all sporting weapons, the center of gravity can be altered by adding a sliding 2 oz (60 gram) weight. Also, the trigger is adjustable and the foresights are interchangeable so that the weapon can be adapted to the skill category. The ergonomic grip is available in left-handed and right-handed versions.
The weapon illustrated has both cocking levers half closed.

This pistol differs radically from most available CO_2 pistols. The gas bottle stands upright below the barrel rather than lying flat. The advantage of this arrangement is linked to the way certain liquefied gases behave. Liquid CO_2 settles at the bottom of the bottle and the gas rises to the top. With a horizontal bottle, liquid CO_2 may escape through the valve into the firing chamber when the weapon is fired, and this can considerably upset the accuracy of the pellet. Keeping the bottle upright gives greater constancy of power and performance.

The system also uses much less gas. This type of tank gives about 150 shots, even though it is smaller.
The weapon can be balanced up by adding a $1\frac{3}{4}$ oz (50 gram) weight to the barrel and a $3\frac{1}{2}$ oz (100 gram) weight to the grip. The ergonomically designed grip can also swivel 10 degrees from normal to fit exactly into the shooter's hand.
This pistol is also available in a short version with an 8-inch barrel (201 mm) instead of 10-inch (263 mm), which is lighter by $3\frac{1}{2}$ oz (100 grams).

CO_2-POWERED PISTOLS

Model C 25 pistol by Feinwerkbau. Powered by CO_2.
7th category weapon.
Pistol firing single lead pellets.
Caliber 4.5.
All steel mechanism, ergonomic wooden grip.
Weight: 2 lb 8½ oz (1.15 kg) (counterweight extra).
Made by Westinger & Altenburger (Germany).

"Distinguished" Trophy Master pistol by Springfield.
1st category weapon.
Sporting pistol, 8 or 9 shots according to caliber.
Caliber .40 Smith & Wesson (available in 9x19 mm, 9x21 mm, 10 mm Auto and .38 Super Auto calibers).
All steel construction, wooden grip plates.
Weight: 2 lb 7 oz (1.1 kg) unloaded.
Made by Springfield Armory (USA).

This pistol derives straight from the 1911 model Springfield, which was the regulation hand gun of the US Army. This classic weapon, which can be made to measure, has an ultra-light, ultra-sensitive trigger. It also has a muzzlebrake (or compensator) which uses the energy of the exhaust gases to stop the weapon kicking when fired. The beavertail in back of the grip also helps with this by pressing down on the top of the hand. The version shown has been fitted with an Aimpoint 5000 telescopic sight.

Practical VB pistol by Bernadelli.
1st category weapon.
Sporting pistol, 12 or 16 shots according to caliber.
Caliber .40 Smith & Wesson (available in 9x21 mm and 9x19 mm calibers).
All forged special steel construction, plastic grip plates.
Weight: 2 lb 7 oz (1.1 kg) unloaded.
Made by V. Bernadelli (Italy).

PISTOLS FOR THE SHOOTING RANGE

This recently designed pistol (1993), created specially for target shooting, invites comparison with the model 19 Springfield. They are similar in design (for instance the external hammer spur, the muzzlebrake, the beavertail and the telescopic sight-mounting) but the VB differs in the combat-style shape of the hammer spur, its much larger magazine capacity and its very rapid rate of fire. It has great customizing potential, with a its reversible magazine button for left or right handers, optional factory-fitted straight trigger, two or four chamber muzzlebrake, checkered walnut grip plates, and so on.

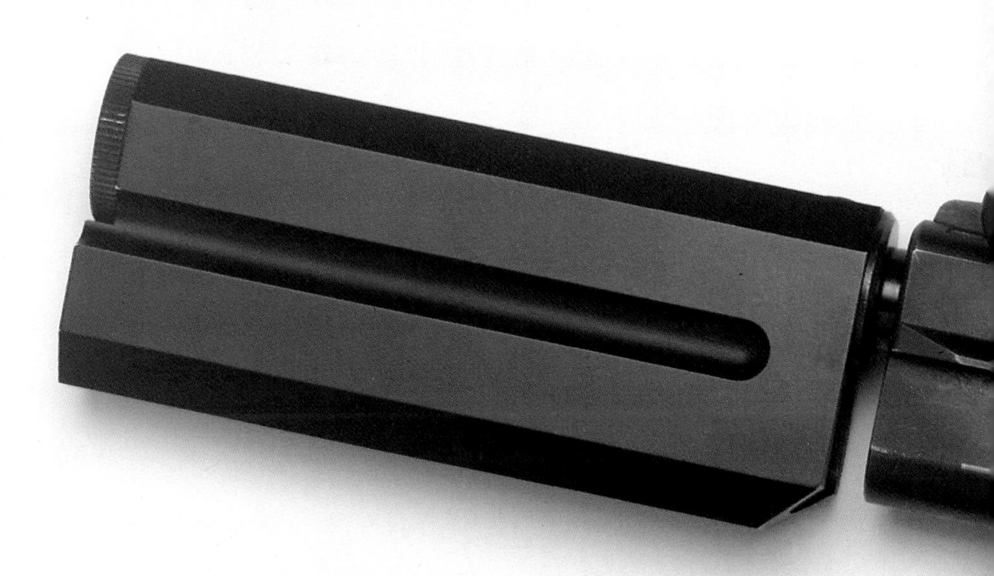

Typical revolver used by police forces across the USA. This one has been modified by fitting a combat grip and an Aimpoint 3000 telescopic sight.

Model 648 revolver by Smith & Wesson.
4th category weapon.
Caliber .357 Magnum.
6-shot.
All steel construction, wooden grip plates.
Weight: 2 lb 3 oz (1 kg) unloaded.
Made by Smith & Wesson (USA).

SPECIALLY ADAPTED MILITARY FIREARMS

Model P 226 pistol by Sig.
1st category weapon.
Caliber 9 mm Parabellum.
15-shot staggered magazine.
All steel construction, wooden grip plates.
Weight: 1 lb 10 oz (740 g) unloaded.
Made by Sig Sauer (Germany).

Originally a military pistol, this one is fitted with a silencer and a laser sighting system. The control button is fixed to the grip plate.

1976
RHODE ISLAND
DELAWARE
PAT. SEPT. 19 1871
JULY 2.72 JAN. 19.75

UNUSUAL FIREARMS

Gun owners and enthusiasts have always been conscious of a weapon's styling and good looks, especially its personalization. This tradition extends to engraved weapons and special commemorative limited editions.

These unusual pistols and revolvers are above all collector's items, carefully arranged in presentation boxes. Even though they work perfectly, their owners hesitate to use them. These weapons are much too handsome to fire!

Metal engraving is one of the best-loved and most widely used forms of decoration. The engraving, which may be entirely by hand on the finest pieces, and sometimes inlaid with gold or platinum, decorates the frame of the weapon. Revolvers also have engraved cylinders that have to be turned slowly to appreciate the full design of the motif. This is often a frieze showing a cavalry charge, an Indian attack, a list of all the states in the USA, and so on.

Grip plates, too, are often decorated with bas-reliefs on a hunting or military theme.

Other unusual weapons are miniature, reduced-scale versions of classic weapons. Though finely executed and in perfect working order, they are not really intended for shooting. But they have the advantage of providing an opportunity to build up a high-quality collection at an affordable price – without taking up too much space.

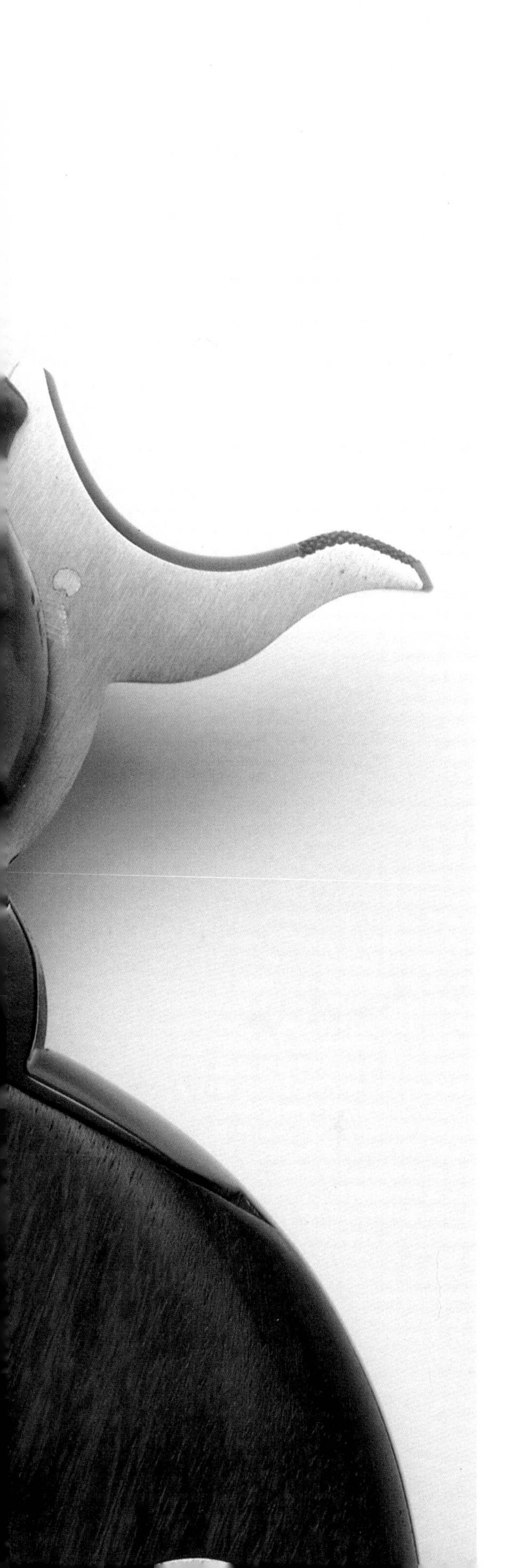

A fine example of engraving on the cylinder of this Colt revolver (highly magnified).

Miniature 1847 Walker Colt revolver.
Made by Uberti (Italy).

Freedom Arms Revolver.
4th category weapon.
Caliber .22 Long Rifle.
5-shot.
All steel construction, wooden grip plates.
Made by Freedom Arms (USA).
This genuine revolver is mounted in a belt buckle.

Cap-firing charm pistol.

Miniature 1851 Navy Colt revolver.
Made by Uberti (Italy).

Miniature 1873 Cattleman-Frontier revolver.
Made by Uberti (Italy).

MINIATURES

Miniature 1860 Army Colt revolver.
Made by Uberti (Italy).

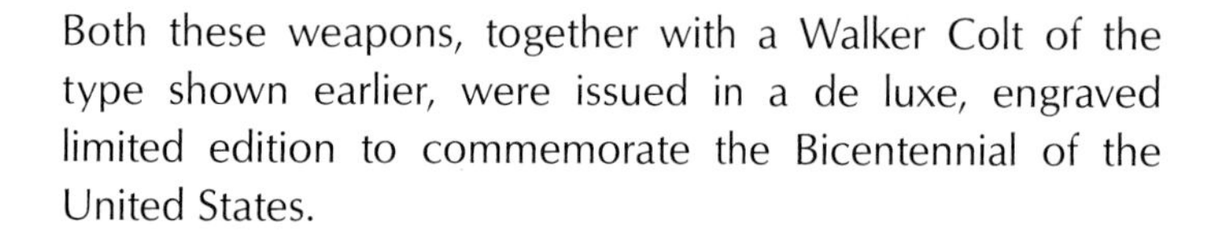

Both these weapons, together with a Walker Colt of the type shown earlier, were issued in a de luxe, engraved limited edition to commemorate the Bicentennial of the United States.

Model SAA 1873 Colt revolver.
4th category weapon.
Caliber .45 LC.
6-shot.
All steel construction, wooden grip plates.
Weight: 2 lb 3 oz (1 kg) unloaded.
Made by Colt (USA).

COLTS OF THE US BICENTENNIAL

Colt Python revolver.
4th category weapon.
Caliber .357 Magnum.
6-shot.
Available with 2 1/2, 4, 6 and 8 inch barrel length (6.3, 10, 15 and 20 cm).
All steel construction, wooden grip plates.
Weight: 2 lb 3 oz (1 kg) unloaded.
Made by Colt (USA).

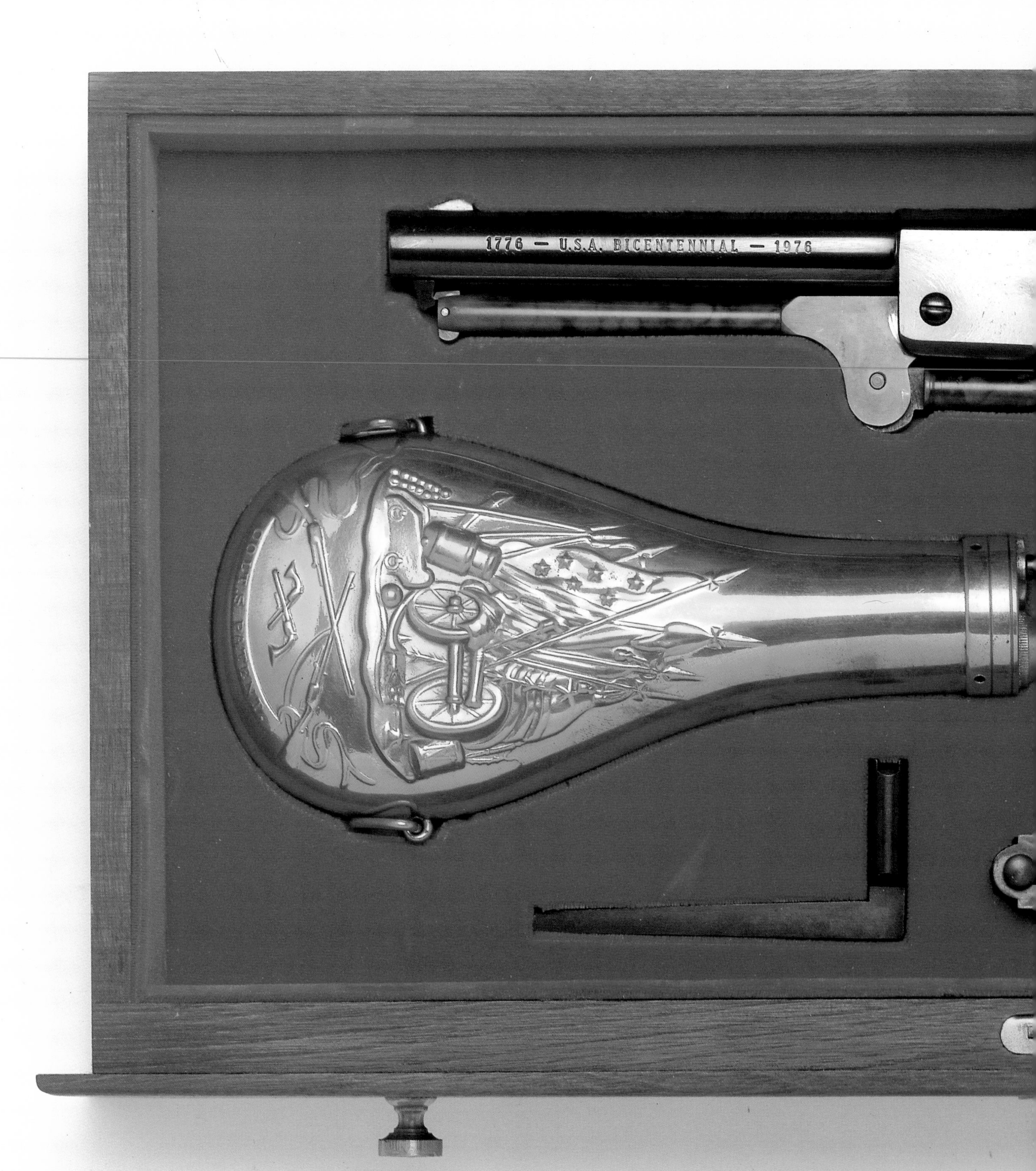

The three Colts commemorating the Bicentennial of US Independence (1776-1976) were issued in a de luxe presentation casket, with each weapon housed in a drawer complete with its accessories. Here is the Walker Colt in its display case.

ELEY BROS
250
METAL-LINED
CAPS,
Made expressly for
COLT'S P^T
Belt and Pocket
PISTOLS.
Manufacturers, London
COLTS
PATENT

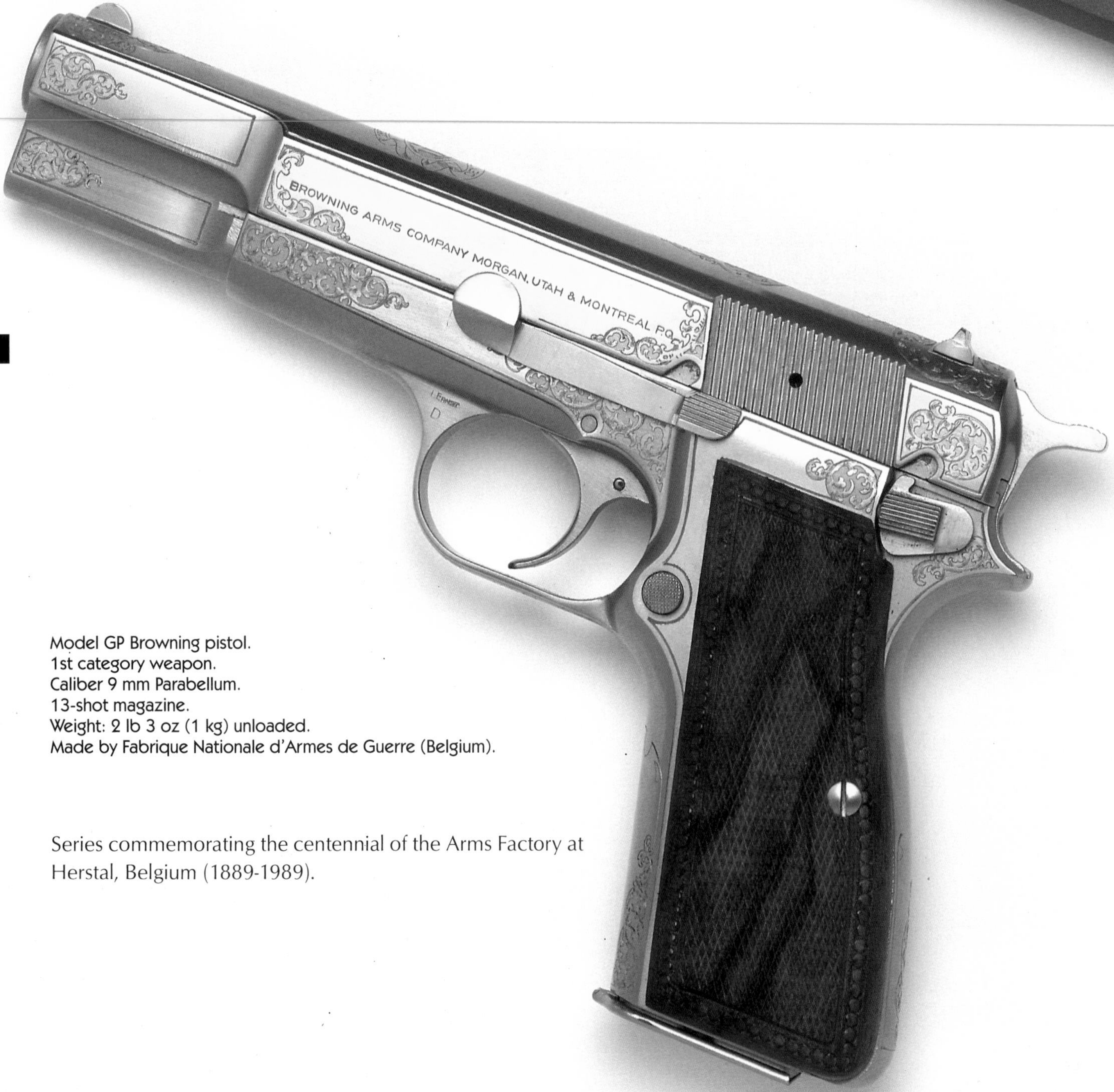

Model GP Browning pistol.
1st category weapon.
Caliber 9 mm Parabellum.
13-shot magazine.
Weight: 2 lb 3 oz (1 kg) unloaded.
Made by Fabrique Nationale d'Armes de Guerre (Belgium).

Series commemorating the centennial of the Arms Factory at Herstal, Belgium (1889-1989).

Model 208 pistol by Hämmerli.
4th category weapon.
Caliber .22 Long Rifle.
8-shot magazine.
Weight: 1 lb 10½ oz (750 g) unloaded.
Made by Hämmerli (Switzerland).

Series commemorating the 125th anniversary of the Hämmerli company.

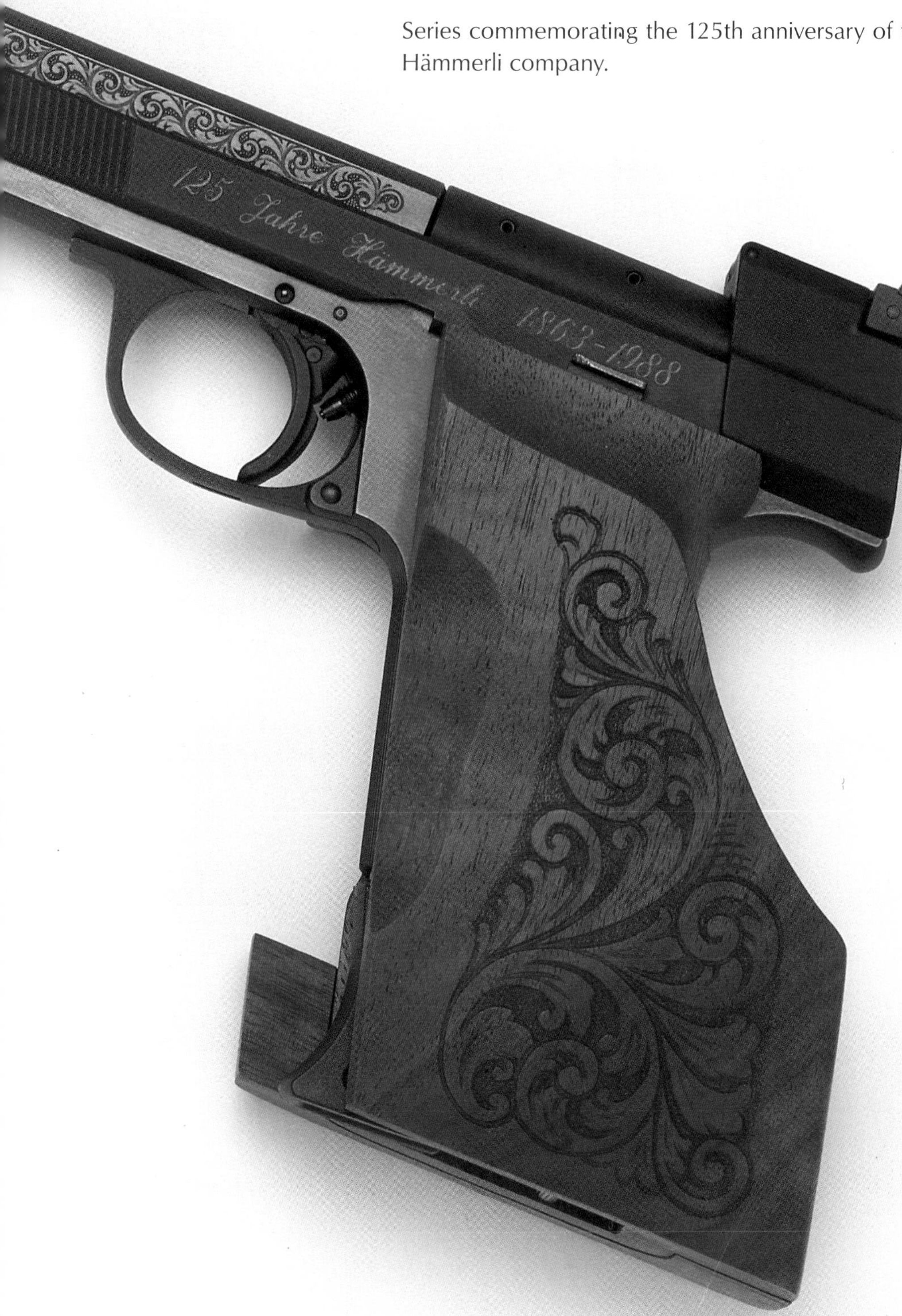

Model P 210 pistol by Sig.
1st category weapon.
Caliber 9 mm Parabellum.
8-shot magazine.
Weight: 2 lb 1 3/4 oz (960 g) unloaded.
Made by Sig (Switzerland).

COMMEMORATIVE LIMITED EDITIONS

Designed in 1947, this single action semi-automatic weapon is standard Swiss Army issue. It formed the basis of two limited editions, one commemorating the 125th anniversary of the Sig company, and the other, the 700th anniversary of the Swiss Confederation.

Reproduction Antique Firearms

These replicas give the enthusiast a chance to collect, so far as the flexibility of the law will allow, a reasonably priced range of firearms based on authentic weapons of the past. Scrupulously made and individually bench-tested just like any other firearm, these are technically and esthetically fascinating reproductions. As often as not, in fact, the replica performs better than the original!

These weapons are not to be confused with certain non-functional, micro-cast replicas of a purely ornamental nature. They are fully functioning, and some of them still achieve top scores at shooting competitions.

All these weapons are black-powder and lead-ball muzzle loaders. They are fired by flint or priming cap according to type. Contemporary accessories, such as a powder horn and ball mold, are also available.

At the present time Italian gunsmiths account for some 95 percent of all replicas made. A few are also manufactured by Spanish gunsmiths.

A word of advice. These weapons are designed strictly for use with black powder. Modern gunpowder, because of its vastly superior burning characteristics, will cause the firearm to explode, with all the imaginable dangers this can represent to the shooter.

Reproduction Derringer pocket pistol with folding trigger, complete with powder horn.
(shown larger than actual size).

Le Page flintlock pistol.
8th category weapon.
Single shot, muzzle-loading, black-powder and lead-ball pistol.
Caliber .45 smooth bore (also available in .44 rifled).
Walnut grip.
Weight: 2 lb 10 oz (1.2 kg).
Made by Davide Pedersoli & Co (Italy).

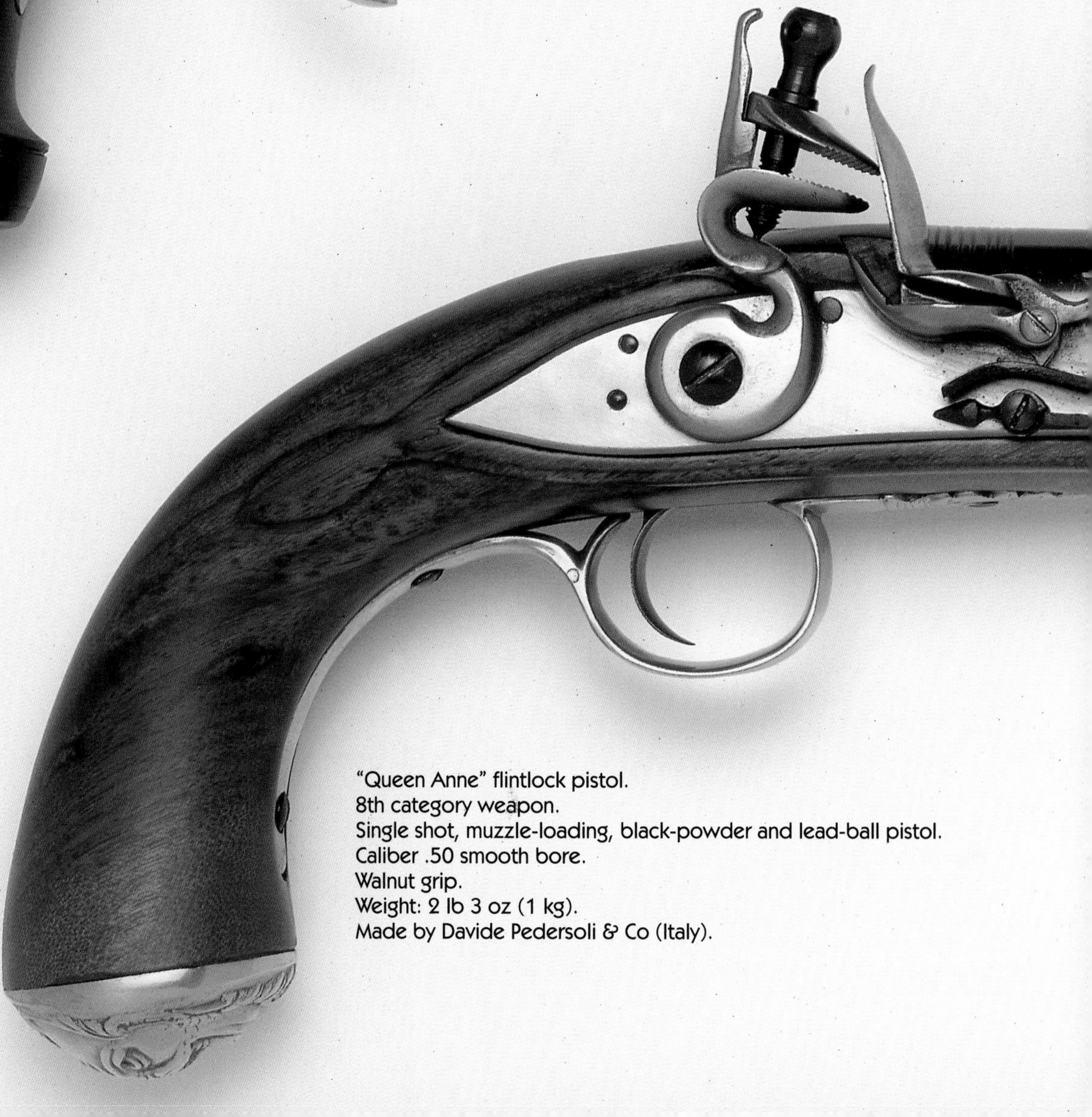

"Queen Anne" flintlock pistol.
8th category weapon.
Single shot, muzzle-loading, black-powder and lead-ball pistol.
Caliber .50 smooth bore.
Walnut grip.
Weight: 2 lb 3 oz (1 kg).
Made by Davide Pedersoli & Co (Italy).

This replica of a duelling pistol made by Parisian gunsmith Henri Le Page between 1840 and 1850 is fitted with an efficient and reliable flintlock. The trigger and sight are adjustable.
This pistol is today regarded as one of the best single shot, black-powder sporting weapons, and has earned a distinguished reputation in the most important international competitions. The roll of honor of shooters using this weapon speaks for itself. World championship: silver and bronze medals 1983, gold medal 1985, silver and bronze 1987, gold 1990; European championship: gold medal 1986.

FLINTLOCK PISTOLS

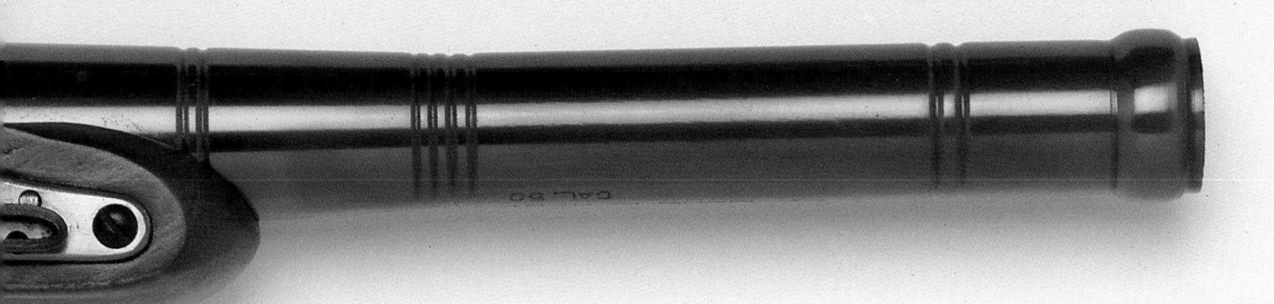

This is an exact copy of the famous flintlock pistol used in England in the late 17th and early 18th centuries during the reign of Queen Anne Stuart (which explains its name).
The flintlock mechanism itself, despite a separation of one and a half centuries, is virtually identical to that of the Le Page pistol. On the other hand, some of the features on the "Queen Anne" are more archaic, such as the brass trigger guard, the absence of any sighting device, and the cylindrical, even slightly conical barrel, shaped and ornamented to resemble the artillery pieces of the time.
In the fashion of the period, the underside of the grip is decorated with a grotesque metal mask.

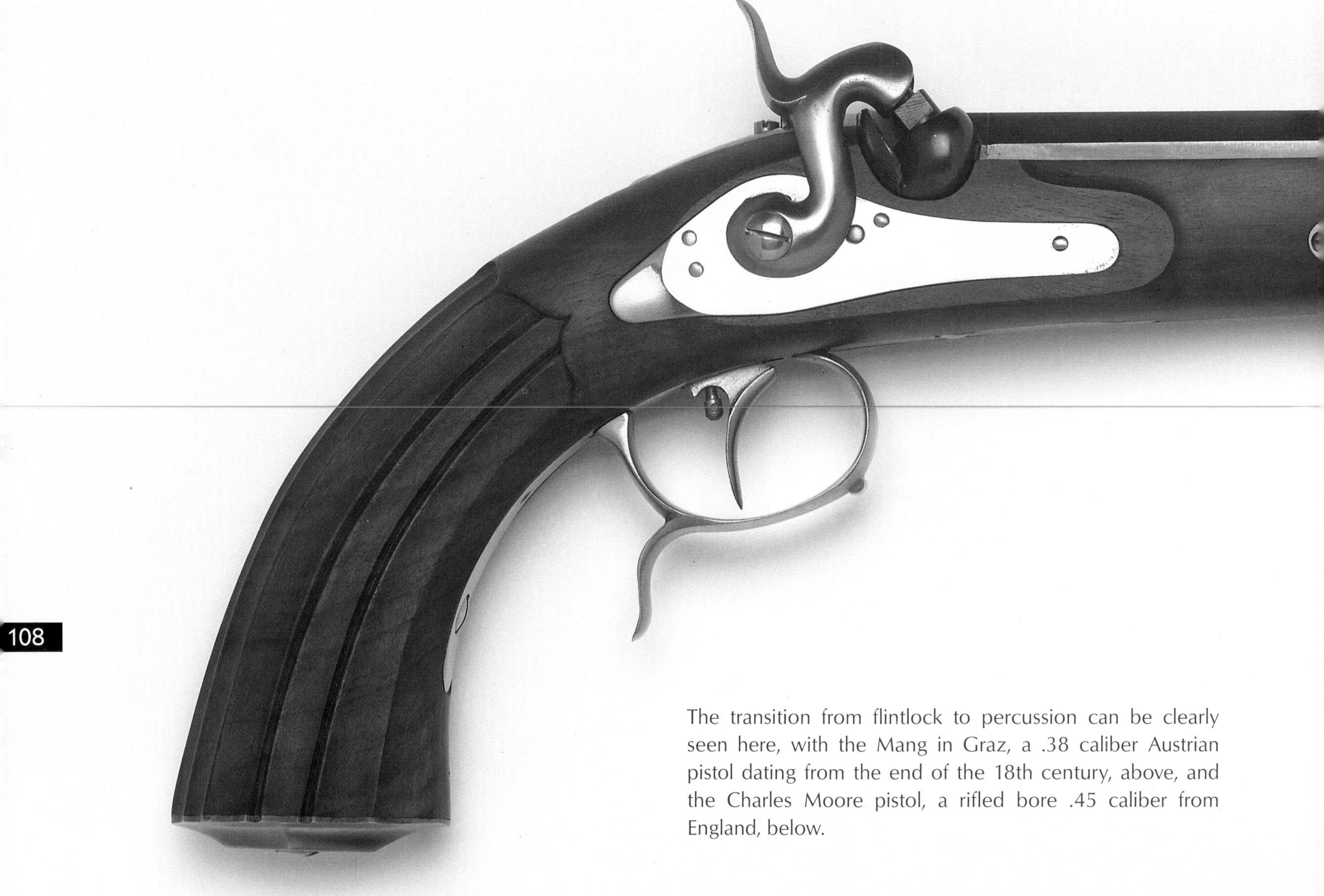

The transition from flintlock to percussion can be clearly seen here, with the Mang in Graz, a .38 caliber Austrian pistol dating from the end of the 18th century, above, and the Charles Moore pistol, a rifled bore .45 caliber from England, below.

FROM FLINT TO PERCUSSION

Double Action Smith & Wesson revolver model N3.
4th category weapon.
Caliber .44. 6-shot.
Nickel plated steel construction, ivory grip.
Weight: 1 lb 12 oz (800 g) unloaded.
Made by Smith & Wesson (USA).

This is a .44 caliber version of the .38 DA created in 1881, and is one of the earliest double action revolvers. With one press on the trigger the pistol is cocked and fired in a very short space of time.

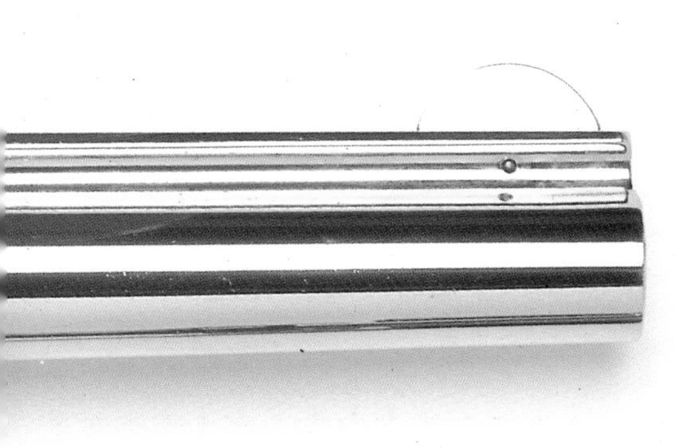

Triple Lock Smith & Wesson revolver.
4th category weapon.
Caliber .44 Special Smith & Wesson.
6-shot.
All steel construction, wooden grip.
Weight: 2 lb 3 oz (1 kg) unloaded.
Made by Smith & Wesson (USA).

This weapon, which was designed in 1908, is fitted with three locks for the cylinder: a front lock, a rear lock and a third lock under the frame, hence its name "Triple Lock." The example illustrated has non-original wooden grip plates.

1836 model Paterson Texas Colt revolver.
8th category weapon.
Caliber .36.
5-shot.
All steel construction, wooden grip.
Weight: 2 lb 10 oz (1.2 kg) unloaded.
Made by Uberti (Italy).

1851 model Northern Reb Colt revolver (the "Sheriff").
8th category weapon.
Caliber .36.
6-shot.
All steel construction ("Southern" version), wooden grip.
Weight: 2 lb 10 oz (1.2 kg) unloaded.
Made by Uberti (Italy).

This weapon was commonly used by both sides in the Civil War. The model illustrated here is the "Southern" version, with its brass frame. The "Northern" version had a steel frame.

WEAPONS OF THE AMERICAN WEST

This is a replica of the first model made by Samuel Colt between 1836 and 1841 in his factory at Paterson, from which it took its name. The Paterson Colt is considered to be the very first really usable revolver. The earliest examples, made between 1836 and 1839, are distinguished by the absence of a loading lever. The cylinder has to be removed in order to reload the weapon.

Designed in 1856 by Jean Alexandre Le Mat, a French doctor living in New Orleans, this single action revolver is unique in the history of firearms. It actually has two barrels of totally different length and caliber. The upper part of the weapon, with the cylinder and long barrel, works like a conventional revolver. The lower part acts as a single shot pistol. To go from firing with the upper barrel to firing with the lower one the nose of the hammer has to be swiveled downward. The idea was probably intended to leave the shooter always with one shot in reserve, even during reloading. The Le Mat was used by the Confederates during the Civil War, and later manufactured in France with even heavier calibers: 11 mm and 24 mm. It seems there were also some Le Mat weapons in 10 mm and 16.5 mm.

Le Mat revolver.
8th category weapon.
Caliber 7.62 mm and 16.5 mm.
9-shot+1.
All steel construction, wooden grip.
Weight: 3 lb 10 oz (1.650 kg) unloaded.
Made by Pietta (Italy).

THE STRANGE CASE OF DOCTOR LE MAT

This weapon, which later went through many modifications and improvements, was among the first military revolvers produced by the Remington company. Elegant and carefully made, it was extensively used by the troops of the Union during the Civil War.

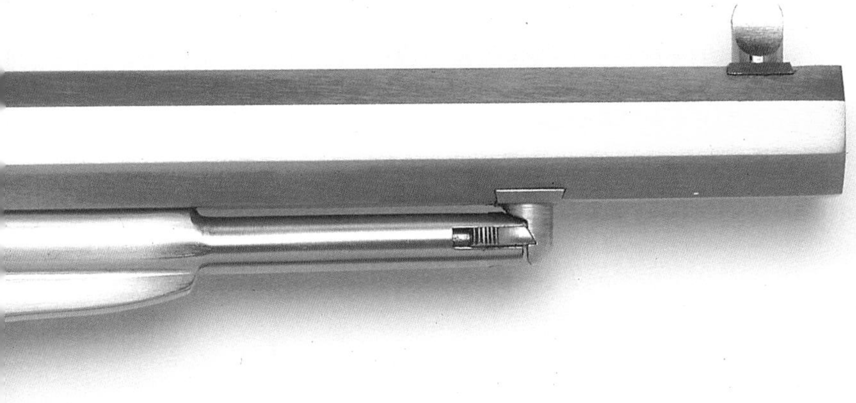

THE CIVIL WAR REMINGTON

The 1858 "New Model Army" Remington revolver.
8th category weapon.
Caliber .44.
6-shot.
All steel construction, wooden grip.
Weight: 2 lb 12 oz (1.250 kg) unloaded.
Made by Uberti (Italy).

1847 model Walker Colt revolver.
8th category weapon.
Caliber .44.
6-shot.
All steel construction, wooden grip.
Weight: 4 lb 3 oz (1.9 kg) unloaded.
Made by Uberti (Italy).

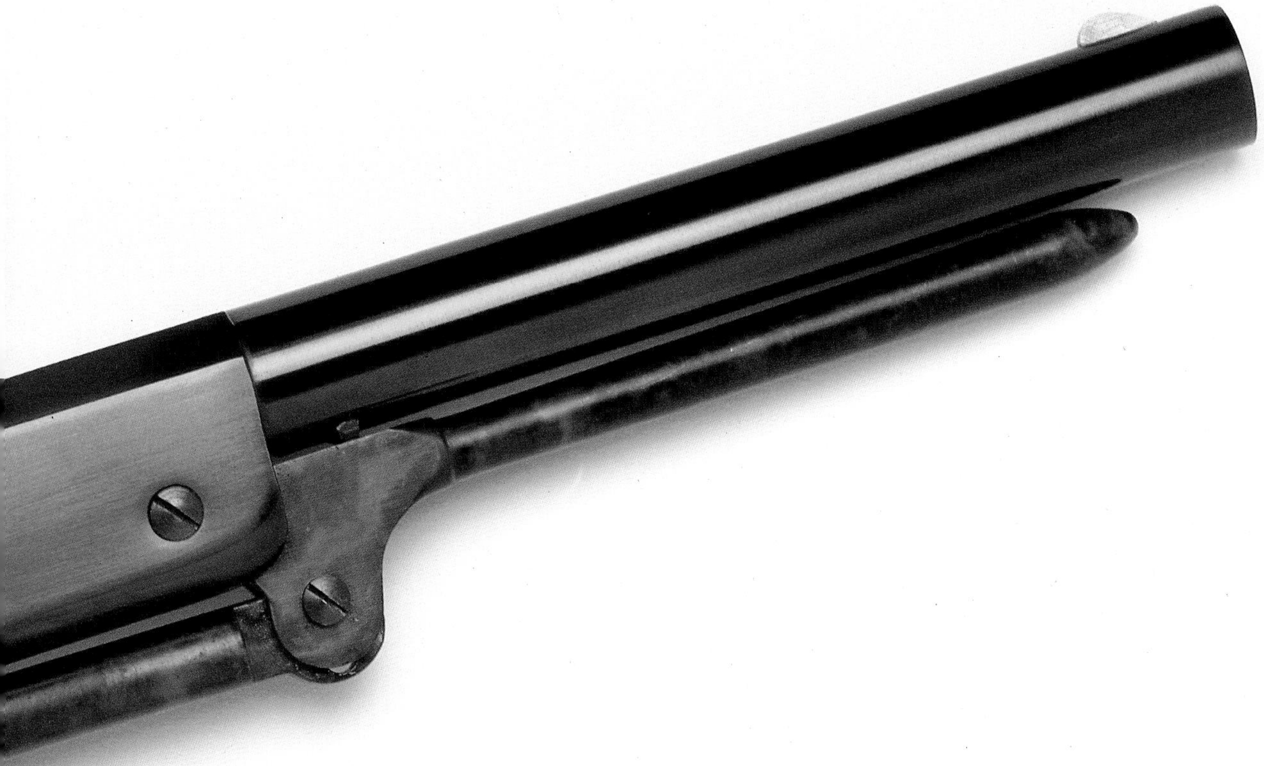

AMERICA

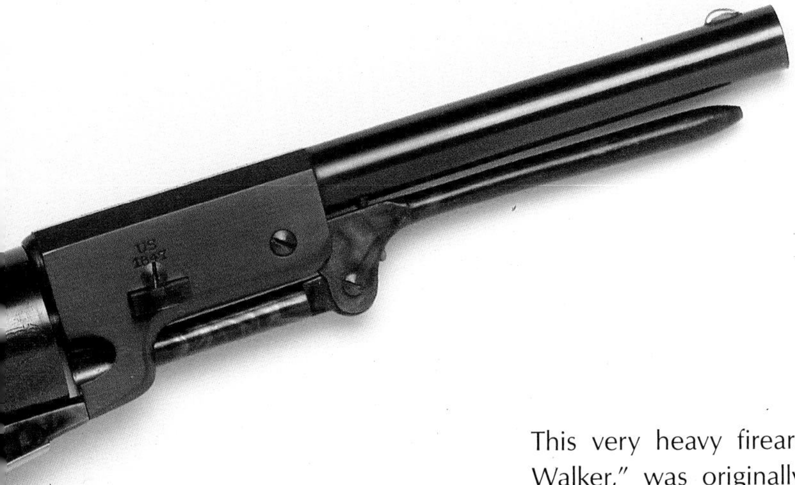

This very heavy firearm, also known as the "Witneyville Walker," was originally designed for the American Army during the war against Mexico. This modern reproduction is shown here together with a miniature version.

NED BUNTLINE COMMEMORATIVE
PAT. SEPT. 19. 1871
JULY 2. 72 JAN. 19. 75

LEGENDARY FIREARMS

Colt, Remington, Mauser, Luger, Smith & Wesson – names we have all become familiar with time and again in books and movies. These legendary weapons are reminders of some technological breakthrough that had a big effect on events of the time. Most were designed at the end of the 19th century, and the principles established then are for the most part still valid.

Some of these firearms were passing fancies, while others are still in use with scarcely a modification. They are all out of the ordinary. Their greatest quality lies in the way they manage to be effective, yet simple to use and maintain. For example, the 1911 Colt shown on page 131, made according to a design dating back to the early 20th century, was still being used in the Philippines as late as 1946, at the end of the Second World War. Whether pistols or revolvers, these weapons have a fascinating history. They have taken part in the great conflicts which have marked and fashioned our age, and their testimony is therefore as important as written documents, though all too often savage in nature. They can enlighten us on the state of international relations, like the Mauser P 08 pistol shown on page 126-127, intended for the Iranian Army and made in Germany in 1942, when the Second World War was at its height.

Until now we have tended to know these weapons by name without knowing what they looked like. Well, now, here they are in all their authenticity.

The dream of the Early West... Ned Buntline commemorative Colt Army model (shown smaller than actual size).

WAFFENFABRIK MAUSER
OBERNDORF A NECKAR

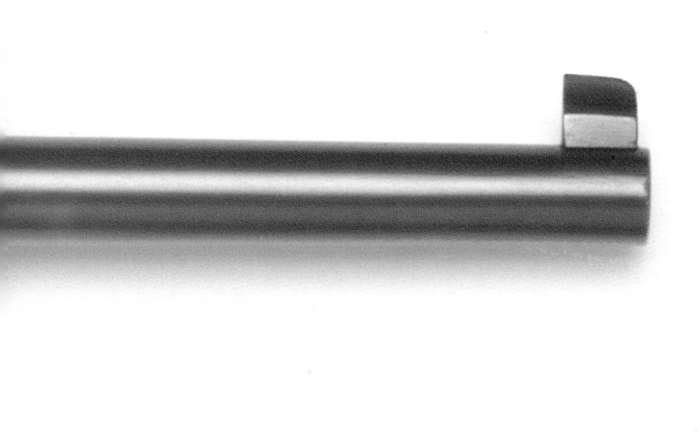

Model MC 96 Mauser pistol.
1st category weapon.
Caliber 7.63 Mauser.
10-shot magazine clip.
All steel construction, wooden grip.
Weight: 2 lb 7 oz (1.1 kg) unloaded.
Made by Mauserwerke A.F. (Germany).

Mauser is one of the most famous names in the world where weapons are concerned. The illustration shows the 1898 model, which improved slightly on the MC 96, and could be fitted to a wooden stock that also served as a holster. This firearm was used extensively during all the armed conflicts of the early 20th century including the First World War.

THE 1896 MAUSER PISTOL

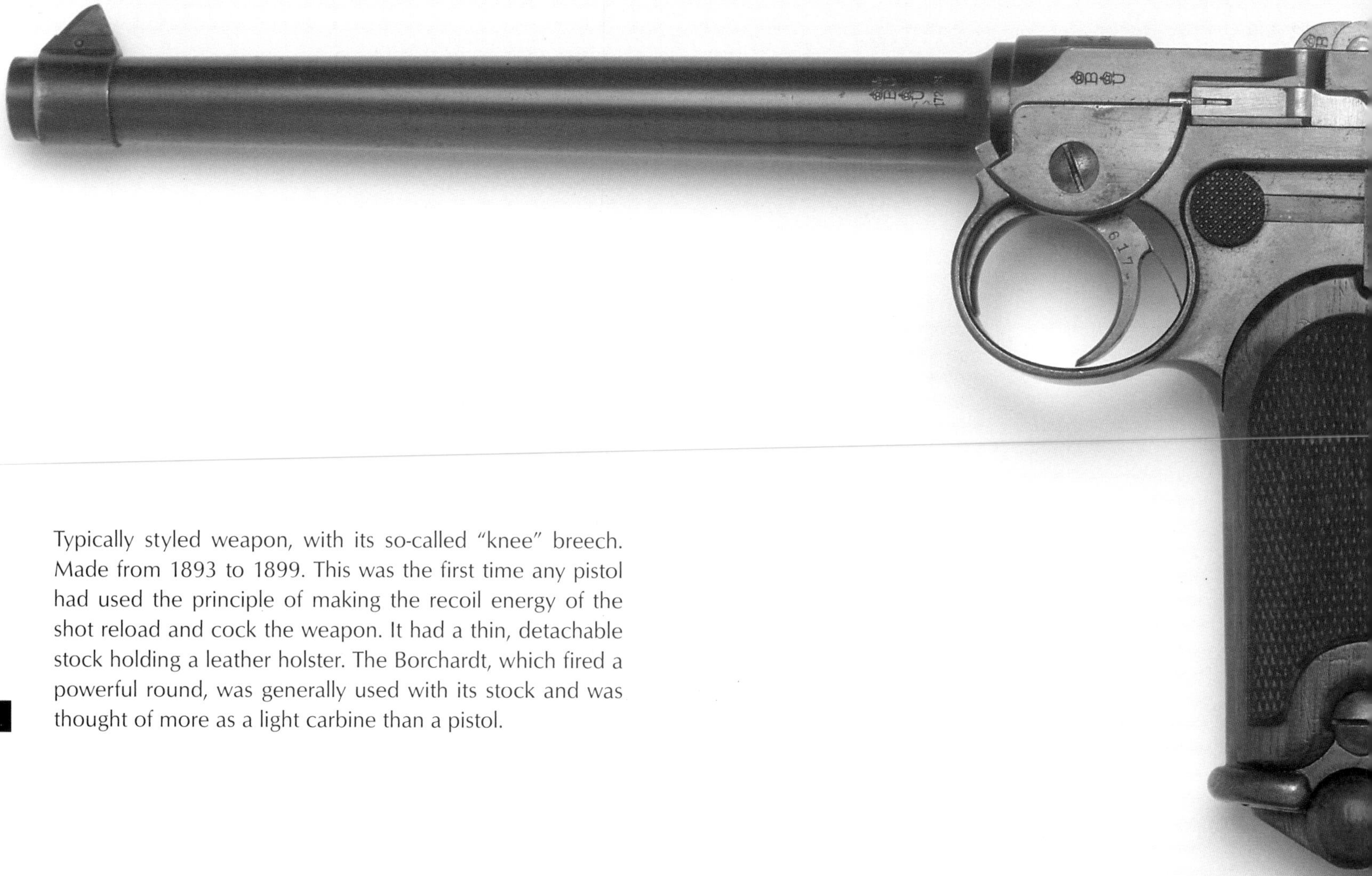

Typically styled weapon, with its so-called "knee" breech. Made from 1893 to 1899. This was the first time any pistol had used the principle of making the recoil energy of the shot reload and cock the weapon. It had a thin, detachable stock holding a leather holster. The Borchardt, which fired a powerful round, was generally used with its stock and was thought of more as a light carbine than a pistol.

Borchardt pistol.
1st category weapon.
Caliber 7.65 Borchardt.
8-shot.
All steel construction, wooden grip.
Weight: 2 lb 10 oz (1.2 kg) unloaded.
Made by DWM (Germany).

THE BORCHARDT PISTOL

More usually known as the Luger (from the name of the engineer who developed the project), the P 08 is a direct descendant of the Borchardt. Originally produced by DWM, it was then made by Mauser up until 1942. This regulation firearm of the German Army and Navy was modified several times prior to 1917. The example shown is a 1917 version, made in 1942 for the Iranian Army, as can be seen from the Persian inscriptions engraved on the weapon. It is fitted with its holster stock and a round, 32-shot magazine.

THE MAUSER P08

Model P 08 Mauser pistol.
1st category weapon.
Caliber 7.65 Parabellum.
7-shot magazine (as standard).
All steel construction, wooden grip.
Weight: 1 lb 14 oz (850 g) unloaded.
Made by Mauserwerke (Germany).

1892 model revolver.
4th category weapon.
Caliber 8 mm.
6-shot.
All steel construction, wooden grip.
Weight: 1 lb 13½ oz (840 g) unloaded.
Made by Manufacture d'Armes
de Saint-êtienne (France).

1874 model revolver.
8th category weapon.
Caliber 11 mm.
6-shot.
All steel construction, wooden grip.
Weight: 2 lb 10 oz (1.2 kg) unloaded.
Made by Manufacture d'Armes
de Saint-êtienne (France).

Black-powder ordnance revolver descended from the 1887 model. It had single and double action, but the double action was very hard to use.

"Officer" version, identical to the 1873 model but for the external appearance. This is an excellent, well-balanced weapon.

1873 model revolver.
8th category weapon.
Caliber 11 mm.
6-shot.
All steel construction, wooden grip.
Weight: 2 lb 10 oz (1.2 kg) unloaded.
Made by Manufacture d'Armes de Saint-êtienne (France).

FRANCE AT THE TURN OF THE CENTURY

Known as the "Chamelot-Delvigne," this black-powder revolver is both single and double action. This regulation infantry weapon brought about a great innovation: the revolver holster.

FIRE ARMS RETENTION AUTHORIZATION
(USAREUR Reg 643-70)

PMO APO 09163
(Name of issuing installation)

DATE 20-9-67

The following weapon has been registered and its retention has been authorized:

Pistol, Automatic
(Type of firearm)

COLT
(Make)

SERIAL NO. 72264

CALIBER

REGISTERED OWNER:

Woodrow (First name) W. (Middle initial) STR

288212 (Registration number) Maj. Gen. (Rank) (SN

Individual named above is authorized by the Commander-in-C... Europe, to ship the firearm listed above to the United States. This do... violate the provisions of AR 643-20.

(Signature of registration official) 1LT MPC, PM (Rank) PMO, APO 09163 (Official station)

PROVOST MARSHAL

AE FORM 11 (29 Aug 66) Previous edition may be used. (See Reverse) L - 8720

Model P 08 Mitchell Arms pistol (new model).
1st category weapon.
Caliber 9 mm Parabellum.
8-shot.
All stainless steel construction, wooden grip.
Weight: 1 lb 14 oz (850 g) unloaded.
Made by Mitchell Arms (USA).

MILITARY PISTOLS

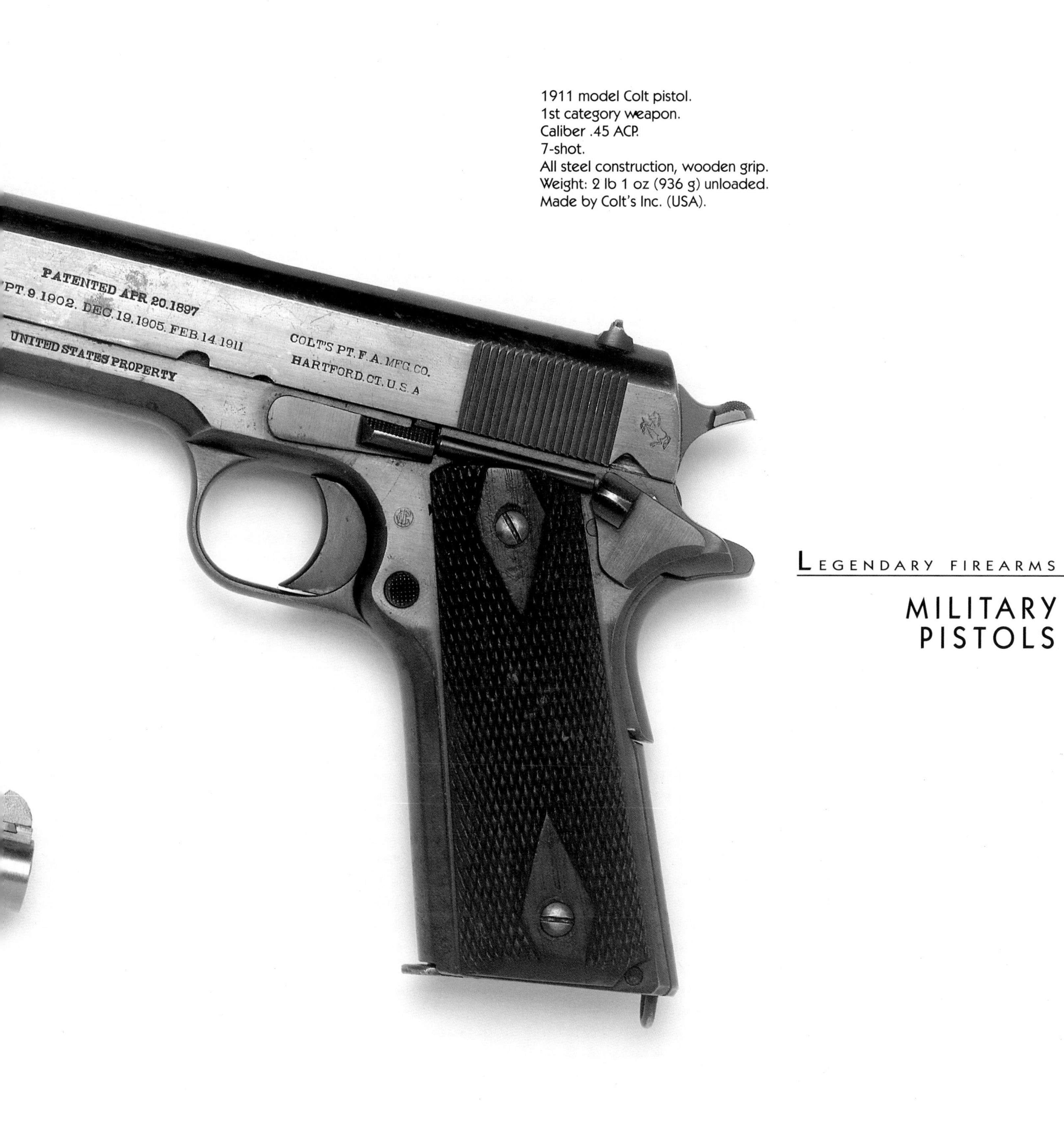

1911 model Colt pistol.
1st category weapon.
Caliber .45 ACP.
7-shot.
All steel construction, wooden grip.
Weight: 2 lb 1 oz (936 g) unloaded.
Made by Colt's Inc. (USA).

One of the best large-caliber wartime pistols in the world, designed by John Browning. Sturdy, reliable, not tiring to use. The example in the illustration is accompanied by a certificate of authenticity showing that it was used in battle in the Philippines during the Second World War.

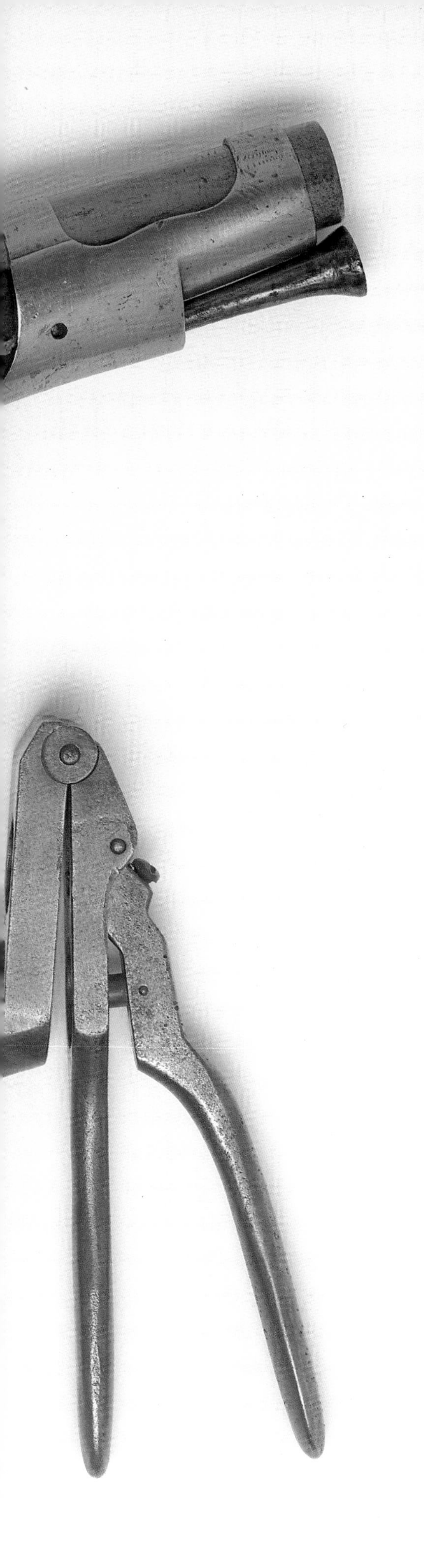

COLLECTING FIREARMS

One of the biggest problems in gun collecting – apart from legal restrictions, overleaf – is ascertaining authenticity. The collector is faced with a fine array of over-restorations, guns assembled from the parts bin, and outright fakes. Then there are deactivated weapons, which make about as much sense as antique motor vehicles with the engines taken out.

The best way to learn to distinguish authentic guns from those which are delicately described as "of uncertain provenance" is to handle as many as you possibly can; or, if you cannot handle them, then at least to examine them in their glass cases. After a while, you begin to acquire a "feel" for what is real and what is not. An authentic gun will always have a patina of age, which may or may not involve much wear: after all, some guns spend most of their lives in their original fitted cases, while others may have had a real working life, with a cowboy on the range or with a soldier in the field. Also, some people are much more careful with their guns than others.

Obviously, check all serial numbers. If the parts are not numbered, examine them for evidence of equal wear and (where appropriate) identical coloring; it is after all quite possible to "repair" many antique guns with parts taken from modern replicas. Examine grips for wear: wood, in particular, acquires a rich patina from years of handling, merely from the skin oils of those who have held it. And (believe it or not), do not neglect the evidence of your nose: old guns actually have a different smell from new ones!

Flintlock pistol, powder horn and ball mold (19th century) (shown smaller than actual size).

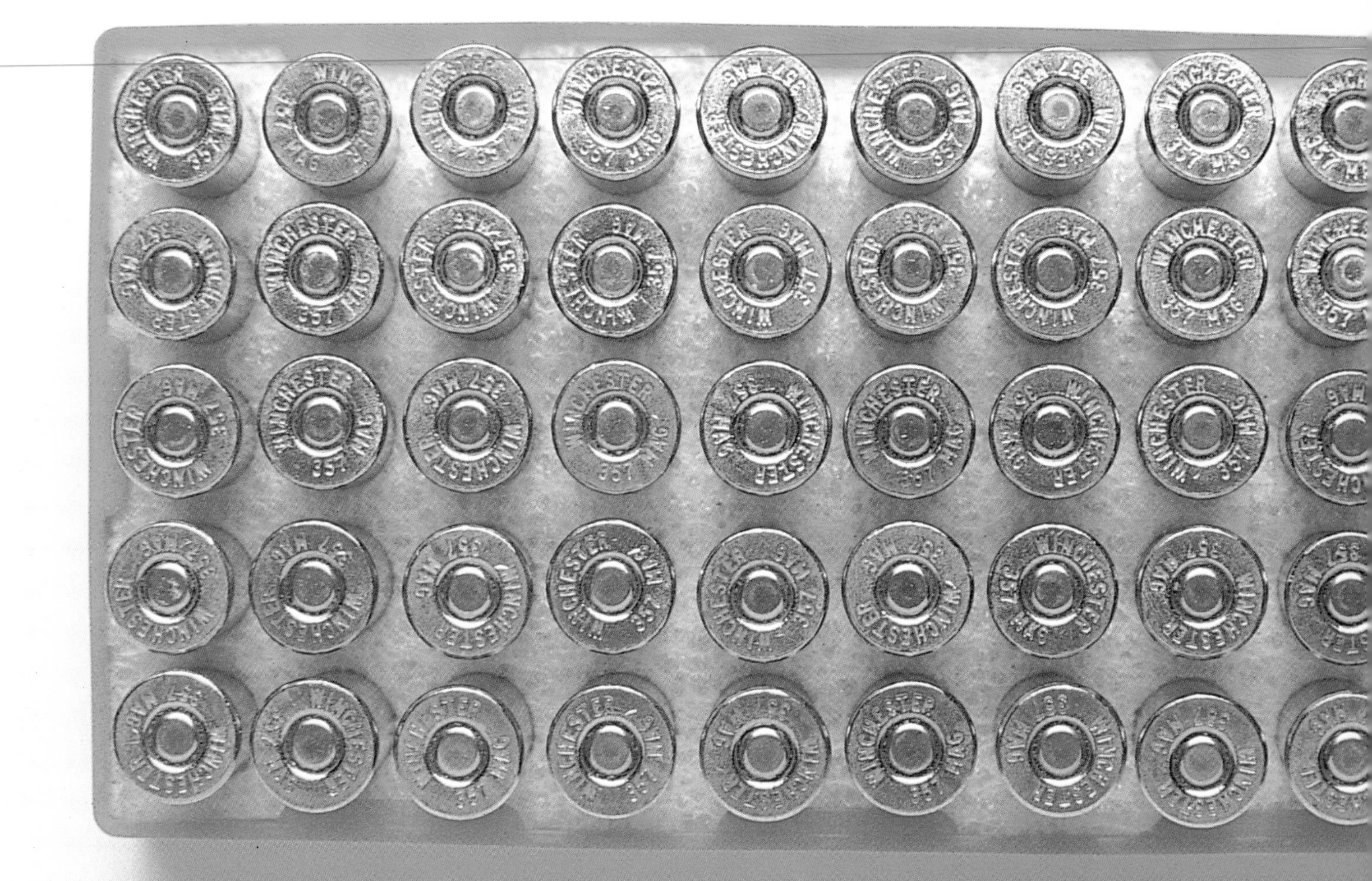
WINCHESTER
357 MAG

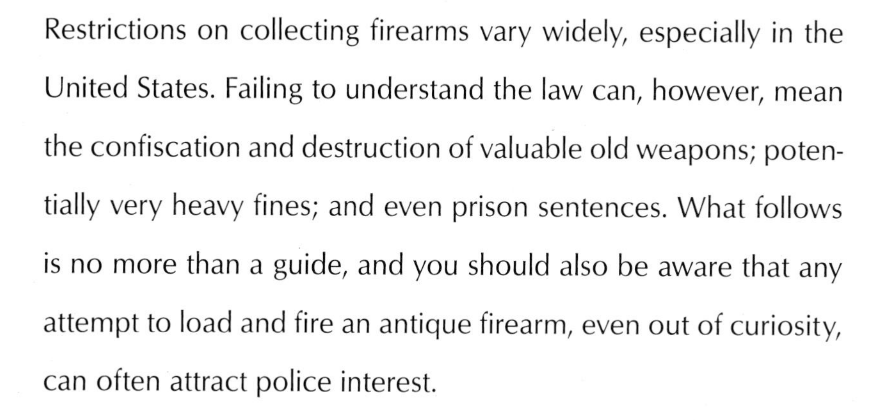

Restrictions on collecting firearms vary widely, especially in the United States. Failing to understand the law can, however, mean the confiscation and destruction of valuable old weapons; potentially very heavy fines; and even prison sentences. What follows is no more than a guide, and you should also be aware that any attempt to load and fire an antique firearm, even out of curiosity, can often attract police interest.

Firearms with few or no problems – Really old guns, kept as "curios or antiques" (to quote England's Firearms Act), will seldom cause any problems. Wheellocks and flintlocks (though not modern replicas) will almost always fall into this categoty, though cap-and-ball percussion guns may fall into this or the next category. A very rough rule of thumb is that the gun must be at least 100 years old, though a certain amount may also depend on the technical and artistic interest of the weapon, as well as upon its rarity.

Firearms with potential problems – Most antique cap-and-ball guns, including those accepting paper or fabric cartridges, should not be subject to restrictions, though you may have to persuade your local jurisdiction of this. Truly obsolete guns accepting metallic cartridges should also fall into this category. Large-bore rim-fire cartridges and pin-fire cartridges normally present the fewest problems. If you possess workable ammunition for any gun using metallic cartridges, including black-powder cartridges, you may, however, find that the gun has to be registered.

Firearms which must normally be registered – Any gun, of any age, for which metallic cartridge ammunition is currently available will usually be treated as a registrable firearm in those jurisdictions which require registration. Modern black powder replica weapons are also normally registrable.

Firearms which are normally banned – Weapons capable of fully automatic fire are very hard to register anywhere, though single-shot (closed bolt) versions of weapons such as the MAC-10 and the Uzi are legal in some jurisdictions. Certain military weapons should be checked carefully to see that they are not capable of automatic fire: check pre-WW2 German pistols in particular. There may also be strange local restrictions, especially on barrel length; technically, a Le Mat pistol could be regarded as a sawn-off shotgun!

ARMURER
BULLETS
COURTY
PONY
FOLDING
Achat d'Armes
ICI

USEFUL ADDRESSES

Few if any museums are devoted soley to handguns, and equally, there are very many museums which are not even devoted principally to firearms which nevertheless have first-class holdings.

In the United States, almost any museum with a military or Civil War collection will have a good collection of handguns; the following are only a selection. The majority of their holdings will date from the 1850s and afterwards, with a few guns from the Colonial period and possibly even earlier.

National Firearms Museum, Fairfax, Virginia
(Closed at the time of writing, but scheduled to open in new premises in late 1994)

American Police Center & Museum, 1717 South State Street, Chicago, Illinois 60603.

Cody Firearms Museum, Buffalo Bill Historical Center, 720 Sheridan Avenue, Cody, WY 82414

J. M. Davis Gun Museum, Fifty & Hwy. 66, Claremore, OK 74017

Federal Bureau of Investigation, United States Department of Justice, Pennsylvania Avenue, Washington DC 20535.

Gettysburg National Military Park, Gettysburg, Pennsylvania.

Kentucky Military History Museum, Old State Arsenal, E. Main Street, Frankfort, Kentucky 40602

Smithsonian Institution, Washington, DC 20560

UDT/SEAL Museum, 330 North A1A North Hutchinson Island, Fort Pierce, Florida 34949

U.S. Marine Corps Museum, and U.S. Navy Memorial Museum, Washington Navy Yard, Washington DC 20374

In Britain, the emphasis is likely to be on much older guns, though specifically military museums will have more modern weapons.

The Tower of London
Imperial War Museum, London
Victoria & Albert Museum, London
The Military Heritage Museum, Lewes, E. Sussex
National Maritime Museum, Greenwich

UN PISTOLET QUI SE RECHARGE SEUL
DES ARMES
Pistolet tchécoslovaque CZ27, de calibre 7,65 mm Browning, à culasse non calée.
Pistolet Unic LC (voir fiche p. 281).
Pistolet réglementaire français 1935-A Calibre 7,65 mm long. Simple action.
Pistolet français MAB modè calibre 7,65 mm Browni
utomatique Le Français alibre 6,35 mm.
FIG. 152
FIG. 154
JIEFFECO (German)
.25 caliber, Vest Pock
Model, magazine capa
6 shots, barrel length
inches, weight 12-3/8
length overall 4-1/2 i
black finish, front and
safety on left side, bl
checkered grips, load
"J.H. CO." in raised
pistol of the time.
Original price (1920's
s combination tool. Car-
st shot. A number of
horn grips.
sent price $20.00
FIG. 155
JIEFFECO (Belgian)
.32 caliber, Pocket
Model, magazine cap
ity 7 shots, barrel le
2-1/8 inches, weight
ounces, length overal
Blue or nickel finish,
left side, loading por
ilar to the Steyr.
Original price $15.00
the side grip and grip safety, trench
port in bottom of handle. Marked
Present price $6.00
S.1878
S&W
VOLVER
A Shop Manu
SIXTH PRINTING
COVERS THE
J, K, L & N ACTIONS
hausen

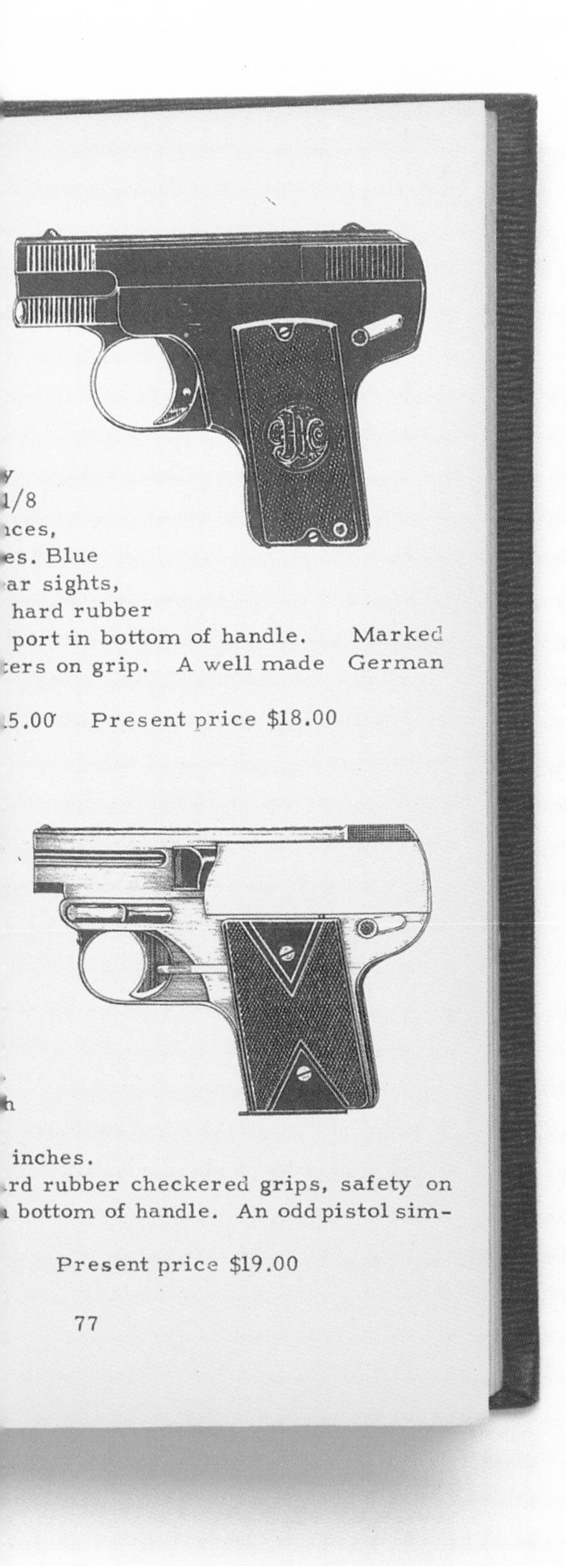
y
1/8
ıces,
es. Blue
ar sights,
hard rubber
port in bottom of handle. Marked
ters on grip. A well made German

.5.00 Present price $18.00

h

inches.
rd rubber checkered grips, safety on
bottom of handle. An odd pistol sim-

Present price $19.00

77

FURTHER READING

Firearms in general, and handguns in particular, exercise a powerful fascination. There are, therefore, countless books of widely varying standards. Information on modern guns is generally harder to find than on older guns, and the following books are among the most useful.

American Handgunner Annual, Publishers' Development Corporation, San Diego, California.

Exploded Handgun Drawings, Harold A. Murtz, Ed., DBI Books, Northbrook IL

Great Combat Handguns, Leroy Thompson and René Smeets, Arms & Armour Press, Poole, Dorset.

Gun Digest – annual, Ken Warner, Ed., DBI Books, Northbrook IL

Gun Digest Book of Modern Gun Values, Jack Lewis, Ed., DBI Books, Northbrook IL

Handguns '94, annual, Jack Lewis, Ed., DBI Books, Northbrook IL

Textbook of Pistols and Revolvers, Major Julian Hatcher. Originally published in 1935 but reprinted several times; currently available from The Border Press in Wales.

Most shooting magazines have articles of interest to the hand gunner, but the following are either dedicated to hand guns or have a higher than usual proportion of hand gun articles:

American Handgunner, Publishers' Development Corp., Suite 200, 591 Camino de la Reina, San Diego, California.

Combat Handguns, Harris Publications Inc., 1115 Broadway, New York NY 10010 (Bimonthly).

Guns & Ammo, Petersen Publishing Co, 6420 Wilshire Boulevard, Los Angeles, CA 90048.

Guns & Shooting, Aceville Publications Ltd., Castle House, 97 High Street, Colchester, Essex CO1 1TH.

Handgunner, Piedmont Publishing Ltd., Seychelles House, Brightingsea, Essex CO7 0NN (Bimonthly).

Chamelot-Delvigne revolver of 1874 (shown smaller than actual size).

INDEX

Acknowledgements

Special thanks are due to Monsieur Pierre Courty and the entire team at the gunsmiths Courty & Fils, 44 rue des Petits-Champs, 75002 Paris, France. Without their kind and friendly helpfulness, confidence and valuable advice this book could simply never have been produced.

Picture credits

All photographs in this book are by Matthieu Prier.